LIKE A
WOMAN SCORNED

BLAKE

Published by Blake Paperbacks Ltd.
98–100 Great North Road, London N2 ONL, England

First published in Great Britain in 1992

ISBN 1–85782–003–7

British Library Cataloguing-in-Publication Data: A catalogue record
for this book is available from the British Library.

Typeset by Falcon Typographic, Fife, Scotland

Printed by Cox and Wyman, Reading, Berkshire

Cover design by Graeme Andrew
Cover illustration by Paul McCaffrey

1 3 5 7 9 10 8 6 4 2

To Toby ..... for doing his homework.

Acknowledgements

I have been given enormous help by a wide variety of people during the writing of this book.

In Britain, I managed to speak to a vast number of policemen, and probation officers and even interviewed Barbara Miller, who killed her love rival and is featured in the story 'The Greenhouse Gallows'.

Others in the U.K. whose assistance was invaluable include Graeme Gourlay, Suzy Davies, Pete Pickton and Sue Carroll.

In America I visited the Dwight Correctional Institute For Women, near Chicago, as well as interviewing the new husband of convicted killer Judy Benkowski.

In Addison, Illinois, Det Sgt Tom Gorniak kindly gave me his time and patience as well as providing never before published photos of a murder victim.

In Los Angeles, Det Mike Lee gave me an unique insight into the disturbing case of The Mall Murders.

In Milwaukee, private investigator Ira Robins aided my enquiries into the Bembenek case.

In Germany, TV journalist Tewe Pannier gave remarkable assistance re the Vienna nurses.

Finally, I particularly want to thank Mark Sandleson for his patience. Without access to his peaceful, quiet office this book might never have been written.

WENSLEY CLARKSON

Wensley Clarkson, author of the international bestseller *Hell Hath No Fury*, (Blake Paperbacks 1991) is a journalist, TV presenter and movie director. Since quitting newspapers full time in 1987, he has also produced a number of British television documentaries and is currently adapting another of his books, *Dog Eat Dog*, into a film screenplay for Twentieth Century Fox, in Hollywood. In 1991, he moved to Los Angeles with his wife Clare and their four children Toby, Polly, Rosie and Fergus.

Foreword

In *Like A Woman Scorned*, I have tried to probe the innermost feelings of the characters involved in each of the awful crimes described here. My intention is to give you a deep, unique insight into these killings.

I have interviewed countless people during the course of my enquiries. But it was the families and friends of the defendants that really provided me with the ability to delve inside their minds and souls to explore the motives behind each killing.

To present a series of crimes in such vivid detail might upset those with a sensitive disposition. Be warned! I have not held back in my quest to present every possible detail – however disturbing.

I have deliberately set out to inform and provoke in the hope that next time such a crime occurs you will start to understand the motivation, however unsavoury, behind it. In trying to present the facts in this dramatic fashion there is no doubt that some readers might discover discrepancies between my version of events and what has been reported elsewhere. I have tried to use only information that I believe to be entirely accurate, but if I have erred in any way then it was in good faith. I have had to make some informed deductions for dramatic purposes. But the actual facts of the cases are as they occurred.

Contents

A Free Trip to God

A strange silence shrouded the grounds of the Lainz General Hospital. It was as if there was no air. Nothing moved. None of the many trees swayed. No-one walked in the grounds. The grey, crumbling façade of the main building contrasted with the pretty apple blossoms dotted throughout the five acres of grassland surrounding the hospital.

Huge ferns cast great shadows on the ornate 150-year-old mansion that had long ago been converted into a centre for the sick and elderly. There was so little sign of life from the outside. So much silence. So much expectation.

The vast gothic windows appeared almost black from the outside. The five storey property looked far taller than it really was. It could have been ten or even fifteen storeys. It had that sort of imposing effect when people visited.

Atop the main frontage were gargoyles – a set of six of them staring intently down on all who entered. A piece of masonry just next to their footage had once crashed down in front of a group of elderly patients. Perhaps it was time for them to leave?

The place exerted a strange emotional pull on anyone who happened to be passing. The sheer enormity of the building. Its long, drawn out features. The lichen-encrusted statues built into virtually every corner. The once pale stonework darkened by a century and a half

1

of grime. Up one side, clumps of ivy clung desperately to powdery mortar.

If it had ever been given the maintenance it deserved, then the Lainz could have maintained its original splendour. It had all the classic ingredients to be pronounced a building of great historical value, but the general public tended to keep well away. A place full of the dying and elderly was hardly going to become a tourist attraction. There was something about it that made the locals suspicious. An aura of death hung constantly around it. Poor souls waiting out their last days in morbid, hopeless circumstances.

When people drove past, it would catch their eye. But only for a second. You wouldn't want to stare too long. All the same, the people of Vienna knew the Lainz General Hospital well. It regularly starred in their news bulletins and featured in the newspapers. But that did not stop it becoming a place to avoid.

Inside, however, it was full of typical, prim Austrian efficiency. The high-ceilinged rooms helped the light pour into every corner. It was clean but the paintwork had certainly seen better days. The walls and corridors had a slightly off white sheen with the occasional damp stain here and there, like a record of all the residents who had come and gone over the years.

The worst thing, though, was the silence.

Of course there were noises. Elevators opening and closing. Trolleys being pushed along the shiny, patent floors. But there was no hum of people. No friendly voices. No childish laughter.

It was like a barrier that hit everyone who entered

that place. First they would be struck by the emptiness in the grounds, then they would be taken completely aback by the lack of voices inside. It was not as if there were no people around. There were nurses, auxiliaries, and porters everywhere. Scurrying up and down the corridors on endless errands. But no-one stopped and smiled. No-one uttered a word. And where were the patients? That eerie silence was the biggest reminder of all. Where were the patients?

A cold, bleak darkness fell on the Lainz General Hospital one day in February 1989. As the day shift staff moved off to their homes in the nearby suburbs they were replaced by the night workers. The men and women whose lives somehow adapted to those strange nocturnal habits. Many of them held together whole families despite the fact they were starting work when most people are thinking about bed.

By midnight at the Lainz, that daytime silence had been completely replaced by an even more sinister atmosphere. Now the sounds of the elevators, the trolleys, and the errands had long gone. But nothing had taken their place. Every now and again a cough or a splutter broke it. But the sound proof doors would smother it, like a hand over the mouth. No-one but the chosen few could possibly know what was going on.

You could walk each and every corridor in the hospital and learn nothing about the patients. They might as well not have existed. And since 80% of the residents of the Lainz were over seventy years of age it was unclear if anyone really cared.

Most of the doctors had long gone. They tended to

work a five day week like any good office worker. Few of them even appeared at weekends. Sickness could wait. If it was an emergency one of the housemen could cope – even though he (or she) may have only just medically qualified. It seemed ironic that the most dire cases ended up being dealt with by the least experienced doctors.

And that attitude was starting to drift through to the nurses. Fewer and fewer of them wanted to work those gruelling night shifts. They were happy to hand over control of the wards to the teams of lowly paid auxiliaries – the men and women who wanted to be nurses but failed to pass (or take) the necessary exams. It was not really the right way to run things, but the system prevailed at the Lainz and no-one really seemed to care.

The silence grew.

Auxiliary nurse Waltraud Wagner was more than happy to take on the additional responsibilities. The fewer bossy nurses patrolling her ward at the hospital the better. The night shifts were bad enough but if you ended up with some Sgt. Major breathing down your neck it would have been intolerable.

In fact, Waltraud rather enjoyed her job as a result. She had much more power and influence than she could reasonably have expected and she was allowed to just get on with her work on the ward – known as Pavilion 5.

Back home, husband Willi hardly inspired her. He demanded food and sex – in that order – most evenings BEFORE she left for work. But she really did not

4

feel in the mood at that sort of time. Her favourite moments for passion came late at night or really early in the morning – but Willi was never around then.

Still, Waltraud understood her husband's frustrations. After all, she was his wife and they had once enjoyed a good sex life. It was just so difficult to explain to Willi. As far as he was concerned, the moment she put on that nursing uniform it was an invitation to lust. But it was nearly always at the wrong time. In any case, she couldn't go to work with a crumpled, messy uniform.

So, over time, as the grind of a night-shift life became ingrained in her system, Waltraud found other ways of satisfying herself.

Julia Drapal had been quite a ballerina star in her day. During the 1950s she had performed at the Vienna Royal Ballet time and time again. Kings, Queens, Presidents – they had all seen her dance.

In Austria, she was as famous as Margot Fonteyn had been in Britain. Julia had been a very privileged person during that period. Chauffeur driven limousines would take her and her husband everywhere. They dined out at the most expensive restaurants. They travelled the world. It was a marvellous time. And it was those very memories that were now keeping Julia alive.

Her frail body had failed her once too often in the previous few years and now she had become a patient at the Lainz General Hospital. She hated it there. But there had been little choice in the matter. The doctors had told her husband she needed full-time medical care. He could no longer cope. She had to be looked after.

But, like anyone who once received the adulation of

millions, Julia was not an easy person to deal with. She had been used to people attending to her every whim. Now she was just another number on a clipboard at the end of her cast iron bed. Her hatred for the hospital and all it represented manifested itself in her attitude towards the staff. In short, she was a cantankerous woman. Given to bursts of insults and bad temper.

Sometimes she would push the nurses away when they tried to tend to her. On other occasions she would try to degrade them by referring to them as 'common people.'

Julia was not exactly the most popular patient on Pavilion 5.

'Time for mouth wash.'

No elderly patient had the energy to refuse when Waltraud Wagner issued orders. Some of the old men rather liked her dominant, strong-willed manner. With her large, round eyes, she certainly looked an attractive proposition to some of those patients. Her uniform always seemed to hug her body in just the right places and those black, regulation stockings – well . . .

But not many of those old men would ever consider actually getting fresh with Waltraud to her face. However, that didn't stop them fantasising about what she might do to them if ever she caught them.

And Waltraud knew full well that some of the men on Pavilion 5 had crude thoughts about her. She didn't mind. In fact, she found it quite flattering. But she did get annoyed when they occasionally tried to molest her.

There was the time the old gentleman in bed number

12 complained of having trouble passing water. When Waltraud arrived at his bedside, he insisted she hold his penis while he tried to urinate. For a few moments, Waltraud obliged until she realised what that dirty old man was really up to. Some of the other auxiliaries used to gossip about seducing the patients.

'I'd marry one of those old sods if they promised to leave me all their money,' said one of Waltraud's colleagues.

She was appalled.

'Oh. I could never do it with an old guy. I don't mind what they are thinking about me but to let them touch me. Uggh. Now if they were under 50 that would be a different matter . . .'

Waltraud had her own strange set of standards in life and they were just as inconsistent as everyone else's.

'Come on now Julia. It is mouthwash time.'

Time to get down to business. Julia Drapal was a bloody annoying patient. Only a few days earlier the old boot had called her a 'common slut' when she had tried to change her bedclothes.

She had decided then and there that Julia definitely needed a mouthwash but she needed a colleague to help her administrate the 'treatment.'

Irene Leidolf tended to work closely with Waltraud because they were two of the youngest auxiliaries on Pavilion 5. At 27, Irene was also a fairly attractive sight compared with many of the other thick set auxiliaries, most of whom were in their late 40s and early 50s. She was much shyer than Waltraud though. She rarely joined in with the gossipy chats

7

they frequently all enjoyed on the ward. But Waltraud liked her because she did as she was told. Irene never questioned any order.

'Come on Irene. Help me give her the mouthwash.'

It was midnight in Pavilion 5, but quite a few of the elderly patients were awake. They watched as the two burly nurses approached Julia's bedside.

It was not a pleasant sight.

Those frail and withered people were about to witness what they lived in fear of receiving themselves – the dreaded mouthwash treatment. No-one knew why it was administered. But they were well aware that it always brought things to an abrupt ending.

Waltraud put a heavily stained plastic glass filled with water to Julia's lips. They would not open.

'Come on Julia. It's mouthwash time. You know you must have your mouthwash. Now come on. Open up.'

Julia was having none of it. She had watched enough beds empty in the previous few months to know that this was not a treatment she wished to receive.

'Right. Hold her down!' Waltraud barked at her younger colleague Irene. 'Come on. We must get this one done.'

She always referred to the patients as if they were more like cows in line for a branding than human beings. Waltraud pinched Julia's nose closed with her thumb and her index finger.

Suddenly a look of complete horror glazed across the old lady's face. Her gaunt cheeks and sagging neck line seemed to stiffen with anxiety. Her eyes were wide open now. Desperately searching for someone to intervene. She tried to move her arms up to ward off the nurse but Irene had both her wrists locked tight.

'Now. You will take the mouthwash won't you Julia.'

There was absolutely no doubt in Waltraud's voice. She knew exactly what she was doing and that made it all the more terrifying for her victim.

As the water slithered down Julia's throat, she tried to cough it back up. For a split second she succeeded in arresting the flow. But the effort proved too much to sustain and her lungs surrendered to the cascade of water that was now pouring down her gullet.

Julia's eyes tried to catch Waltraud. They tried to appeal to her to stop. But Waltraud had deliberately blanked her expression. She was staring at the wall behind the bed. She did not want any emotion to impinge on the horrifying reality.

The only noise that could now be heard was the slight gurgle when Waltraud forced too much water too quickly down her patient's throat. She responded by slowing down slightly. It was imperative that the water filled those lungs to bursting point. It would not be long now. It would not be long.

Irene Leidolf stood there holding down this frail old lady without really giving any thought to what she was doing. She had a family to feed and she wasn't going to put her job on the line by refusing to help Waltraud. In any case, Julia's time had come. It was as simple as that. Her attitude was no different to the guards at Auschwitz. It came as second nature to follow orders. Why question them and upset the apple cart. Life had to go on . . . for some.

Waltraud had by now emptied the entire contents of that glass of water down Julia's throat. She released her hold on her tiny, limp nose.

'There. That wasn't so bad was it?'

9

If Julia had had the energy to speak she would have cursed Waltraud to a thousand deaths. Instead, she knew her own demise was imminent.

As Waltraud walked back towards her desk she turned to Irene and said: 'There. That's another one who has got a free trip to God.'

Coughing and spluttering, Julia could feel the darkness setting in. The pain in her lungs was so great it was as if someone had forced an iron bar down their entire length. Her arms were no longer being held down by Irene, but they might as well have been. There was no strength left in them. Her head slumped to one side and she stared out along the ward to where Waltraud and Irene were sitting. They seemed to be sharing a private joke. Maybe they were talking about her? She realised with a jolt of finality, that she would never be able to find out.

The pain in her lungs was awful. A stabbing sensation had taken over now. Breathing seemed like a great labour, something unnatural to her body. She just wanted the agony to end.

As the last few minutes of her life ticked away, her thoughts of fighting and her sense of survival were all but fading. Julia had lost her last battle, and cursed her last nurse.

*   *   *

'It's one of the patients. I think she's dead.'

Some hours had passed since Waltraud had administered her mouthwash treatment. Now Waltraud was telling the duty doctor that his services were required.

10

'I'll be there in about thirty minutes. There's hardly any point in rushing.'

Pronouncing a patient dead was not exactly classified as an emergency in a hospital like the Lainz. In any case, water in the lungs was a common contributory cause of death amongst the elderly. The doctor would not even raise an eyebrow at the discovery of the liquid. Waltraud knew. She had done it so many times before.

Waltraud then casually drew the curtains around Julia's bedside. Ironically, it was that very action which told the other patients they had lost another resident. If those curtains had never been drawn, probably they would never have known. But now it was being advertised in vivid detail. Another desperately needed bed for another hopeless case. For most of the patients who entered Pavilion 5 had little or no chance of survival. Waltraud Wagner and her colleagues would see to that.

Waltraud was troubled by one aspect of this deadly scenario – why did she enjoy it so much? Each time she snuffed the life out of yet another Pavilion 5 patient it prompted a surge of satisfaction. A feeling that made her immensely proud. Maybe it was something to do with the power it gave her? Or perhaps she actually felt like a true angel of mercy – putting all those bleak, worn lives to rest for ever?

The afterglow would stay with her for hours after a killing. She would arrive home at her flat at six in the morning elated by the horrendous act she had just committed.

'How was work darling?', her husband would ask innocently through his sleepy haze.

'Oh. Fine', she would reply. Waltraud could hardly

11

describe her working night as an auxiliary nurse as 'wonderful' to her husband, but that was precisely how she felt. A radiance would illuminate her soul.

It was at moments like that she would give her husband the sex he had craved for most the previous nights. Often, Waltraud would not bother taking her uniform off – she knew he liked it that way.

Unbuttoning the front of her tunic and exposing her breasts would be enough for him to know what she wanted.

'It's so easy. And they'll never know we did it.'

Waltraud Wagner was enjoying a rare evening out at a local beer cellar with her co-conspirators Irene Leidolf, Maria Gruber and Stephanie Mayen.

The four women had decided they deserved a night on the town – after all they had managed to murder nearly fifty patients over the previous five years. The truth was they had stopped counting long ago. The numbers really began to increase after Waltraud devised her mouthwash treatment. That was so much easier than injecting huge amounts of insulin.

Stephanie was far older than the other three and seemed to fit the role of a ferocious, bulky auxiliary far better than her younger colleagues.

Yet, ironically, she was the more hesitant member of this self-professed chapter of the Angels of Death. Maria – a heavy set women in her early 50's – was appalled when she first realised what was happening. But then Waltraud started to convince her they were doing all these elderly, infirm patients a favour.

12

'In any case. Some of them are so bloody annoying they deserve it.'

Chilling words from the ringleader. But the other women were not about to argue with her. They were all in this together.

In that lively basement beer cellar that night, the four women were off duty for once. There would be no distant cries in the night. No incontinent old men. No senile dementia. For once, they were together outside work – and they were determined to have a good time.

When Irene and Waltraud caught the eye of two businessmen types in the far corner of the cellar, they returned their glances provocatively. These women were out to enjoy themselves after many months tolling in the killing fields of Lainz General Hospital.

The beer and wine flowed freely as did the talk that evening. As usual Waltraud was the one holding court. She craved for attention wherever she was. In the hospital she loved the fear she induced among the more timid patients. She relished in her display of power over them. She could decide whether they lived or died. It was an amazing feeling.

It was exactly the same in that bar cellar. She wanted to be the one in charge. She would love to look at all their attentive faces lapping up every word she uttered. She knew she had them under her spell.

She decided to put them all to a little test. A way to see just how loyal they really were.

'None of you ever say much about what we have done. Why not? Are you not proud of the fact we have put those awful sick, elderly people out of their misery?'

The other women said nothing. They did not know how to respond. Doing it was one thing. But facing the reality of their actions by talking about it openly outside work seemed too much to contemplate.

Still they were silent. For a moment that same eerie silence that haunted the corridors of the Lainz had returned. It was a significant silence though. For it showed how little these women had even questioned their own killing instincts. They had stifled the life out of all those countless patients – and yet they could not even contemplate talking about it. Waltraud was appalled.

'Come on. What do you really think about what we have done? Tell me.'

No response. They really did not know what to say. Here they were being confronted with the facts but they were afraid to speak – much more afraid than they were to kill.

'Let's talk about something else.'

At last, a reaction. Stephanie at least made her feelings clear. She may have helped murder a lot of innocent people but she certainly did not feel it made for good dinner table gossip.

'But we have killed all these people. You must feel something about it? Don't you love the power we have? The influence?'

It was time to change the subject. Waltraud had just discovered that her co-conspirators were nothing more than sheep. Nothing more than Nazi troops doing their duty. They had no feelings.

But someone nearby had heard every word of their conversation – and he was about to try and end their murderous reign of terror.

Dr Franz Pesendorfer was horrified by what he had

14

just heard. Sitting near the group of auxiliary nurses had just revealed one of the biggest mass murders in post-war Europe. The doctor went straight to the police.

Waltraud was a little surprised by the recent changes at Pavilion 5. Some of the newest patients seemed to be rather young – in their 60s and even one in his 50s. This was supposed to be a geriatric ward after all.

She sensed something was not quite right but she just could not be sure what it was. Her basic instincts told her to be careful. She decided the killing had to stop for the time being. It was not as if they were making any money out of the slaughter of the innocent.

It was purely a way to relieve some patients of their agony and get rid of others who had annoyed them by being rude. That was cold blooded murder. No real motive other than the inbuilt sense of power that came with every killing. Anyway, Waltraud decided she should slow down – just in case. Just in case someone had told on her.

The 'younger' patient was indeed an unhappy resi-dent at the Lainz. He hated every second of his stay in that smelly, rotten Pavilion 5 ward. All the nursing staff had quickly grown to dislike him about as much as he loathed them. By a strange twist of fate, if he had been a little older and Waltraud had not been on her guard, then he would definitely have been a candidate for the mouthwash treatment.

In fact, he was a very miserable undercover police-man, planted inside the ward after Dr Pesendorfer had tipped off the Vienna Detectives Bureau following the conversation he had overheard at the beer cellar.

At first the detectives had been scathing about the good doctor's fears. But the hospital administrator had friends in high places so they were forced to respond.

'Old people do tend to die.'

The detective who originally dealt with the case was just a bit cynical. He could not believe that a few women auxiliaries would cold bloodedly murder all these people.

'How can we prove it?'

There was only one way. They would have to be caught in the act.

But Waltraud was on her guard. She knew like all good criminals that something was not right on Pavilion 5 – and she would not risk another kill while the situation prevailed.

Meanwhile, the undercover policeman got more and more depressed. Sleeping in a ward surrounded by dozens of coughing, farting, snoring, groaning old people was not his idea of a plum assignment.

It was hardly surprising when the Vienna Detectives Bureau called off the case following six weeks without so much as a hint of a killing. The good Dr Pesendorfer was stunned that the police were pulling out.

'But you are just allowing them to carry on.'

The policeman was sympathetic to the doctor's plight but he reckoned there were some real criminals out there who needed catching.

*   *   *

Waltraud knew it. She had suspected there was something odd about him from the start. When the news swept around the hospital that an undercover policeman had been a patient on Pavilion 5, it came as no great surprise.

But now he was gone. His tail firmly between his legs. None the wiser for his awful stay in that depressing ward.

It was time to begin the killing again. She felt the urge. She had earmarked the most likely patients. The ones who had annoyed and insulted her. The pathetic ones who were ready to curl up and die. It was so easy really. The fully trained nurses were never around. They did not care what the auxiliaries did. It had got to the point where no-one ever questioned the right of those under-trained assistants to administer drugs and hand out other treatment. That was why Waltraud and her friends had got away with it for so long.

As Waltraud pressed her thumb down on the syringe, she watched the huge dose of insulin rushing into a patient's sickly vein. The elderly women had asked for pain relief so why shouldn't Waltraud give her the ultimate cure – death?

She had grown a little bored of administering the mouthwash. In any case, if there were any spies left on the ward they would be more likely to notice two nurses holding down a patient than the giving of an injection.

'Nurse. Nurse. Has this patient been given any insulin in the past three hours?'

Waltraud looked the young doctor straight in the face.

'No doctor. Not a thing.'

She gave the medic one lingering glance up and down. He is quite a fine looking man, she thought to

17

herself. The welfare of patients was never near the top of Waltraud's list of priorities.

She much preferred to let her mind wander in a world of sexual fantasy. It was so much less depressing. That same elderly women who had been given a huge dose of insulin just an hour before, was close to death – and Waltraud knew it only too well.

Now this rather handsome young doctor was asking awkward questions. How annoying of him, thought Waltraud Wagner. Why doesn't he just let her die? It would seem the sensible course of action.

In any case, in a few more minutes she would be dead – and no-one would be any the wiser. Waltraud's mission of murder was on course once more. She had regained the taste for killing after a brief interruption. It was a good feeling. She would have to try to step up the rate. She found herself needing a fix more and more often.

The doctor, however, had other plans for Waltraud. He was very unhappy about that elderly woman's death. He suspected she had been administered an illicit dose of insulin.

Waltraud presumed he was just a fussy medic trying to cover his own inefficiencies.

'They know. They are on to us.'

Waltraud dismissed the alarm bells ringing in her colleagues' voices when they cornered her a few hours later.

'Don't worry. That doctor thinks he will be accused of not looking after his patient properly.'

Though the other women were not convinced, they

18

had no choice but to accept what Waltraud told them. She held the key to their fate.

Meanwhile the good Dr Pesendorfer had got involved once more. He had never dropped his initial suspicions about the women. Now he was hoping that this new case might be just the breakthrough he had been hoping for.

'I know they have murdered a lot of patients. We cannot let this continue. We must stop them.'

They were the same words he had first uttered two months earlier after overhearing their beer cellar chat. But this time he felt certain they would be brought to justice. He hated the very notion of knowing that five women who had murdered tens if not hundreds of patients still had the free run of the hospital. It was a scandalous situation he was determined to end.

When the autopsy on the elderly woman revealed her body to be riddled with insulin the police were called back into the Lainz General Hospital and Waltraud Wagner and her three accomplices were arrested.

Wagner, Leidolf, Mayen and Gruber were jailed for their roles in the murder and attempted murder of 42 patients at Lainz following their trial in Vienna in March, 1991.

Wagner collapsed in court as she was jailed for life. She had confessed to 10 killings, been found guilty of 15 cases of murder, 17 cases of attempted murder and two cases of inflicting bodily harm.

Leidolf was also given life for five cases of murder and two cases of attempted murder.

Mayen was jailed for 20 years for a case of manslaughter and seven cases of attempted murder. She too collapsed in the dock and had to be taken out on a stretcher.

Gruber was sentenced to 15 years for two cases of attempted murder.

Wagner had claimed during the trial that she was 'relieving the pain of patients.'

The Judge told her: 'These patients were gasping for breath for up to half a day before they died. You cannot call that pain relief.'

Wagner did not reply.

The First Day of the Rest of my Life

They looked every inch the happy couple.

She was blonde, slightly round-faced. With her long hair swept back off her forehead, maybe she more resembled a member of the swinging sixties than the 1990s, but there was a definite attractiveness about her. Despite being just 29 she also had a certain homeliness that comes with being a young mother. It was a pleasant enough combination.

He was tall and dark with a neatly trimmed moustache. Well built. Even slightly cumbersome. He often looked less than his 35 years. And the only real clue to his profession were his hands. He had large, stubby fingers with incredibly short nails – a sure sign of his work as a labourer.

Paul and Pamela Sainsbury hardly warranted a second glance inside the crowded *Carinas Nightclub*, in the picturesque seaside town of Sidmouth, in Devon. As the soul music throbbed relentlessly from the huge speakers that hung on every wall, the scene resembled a cattle market. For it was the *in* place for anyone under 40. Groups of men and women would swarm into *Carinas* on a Saturday night looking for fun and excitement. Many of them were also looking for sex.

Gangs of young men would patrol the disco floor looking for suitable girls to ask for a dance, many of whom had their own secret code that would pronounce their availability. If they were looking to be picked up, they would stay huddled in little groups near the dance floor, sipping slowly on their rum and blackcurrants in the hope that some white knight would ask them for a dance and maybe even offer them a refill.

Other groups of women, intent on just enjoying each other's company, would go straight out onto the dance floor and put their handbags on the floor between them as they danced to the music. It was their special way of saying 'We are not available.' Sometimes they would dance for hours, perfectly happy not to attract the company of any males. Meanwhile, those predatory guys would be filling themselves up with lager – the staple diet of 90% of all men in that club on most nights.

All this meant that by about 11pm, there were always quite a lot of inebriated people in *Carinas* – and this particular evening was no exception.

Paul Sainsbury may have had his pretty wife Pam for company but that didn't stop him supping a lot of pints that night. It was his idea of a good night out. In any case, *Carinas* meant something really special to them – it was the place where they first met eight years earlier. It held a lot of sweet memories for Paul. It reminded him how lucky he was to have Pam. How fortunate he was that she was the mother of his two children.

Yes, Paul really did appear to have a domestic set up that was the envy of many of his friends. And, as he sat with Pam and a few of their local pals at a table near the dance floor, he was no doubt able to reflect on that good fortune. For many of his male friends were still reduced to trying to pick up women in *Carinas* or any other club for that matter. It was something he did

22

not need to concern himself about. He had Pam. He really loved Pam. She was his life and soul. She was the perfect reflection of his inner self. She understood his weaknesses and nurtured his strengths. They were good together.

Pam, meanwhile, was delighted to be at the nightclub. It was a rare excursion out of the house for her. These days she hardly ever seemed to get out. Maybe, she thought to herself that evening, maybe I should try it more often.

It was difficult to converse above the throbbing beat of the disco, so Pam and Paul found themselves looking around the club, inspecting the vast crowd – many of whom they knew. After all, Sidmouth is one of those sort of places. Most people know each other, even if it is only by sight. And a lot of the men and women gathered at *Carinas* that night had virtually grown up together. They had gone to the same schools. They had drunk at the same bars and they often went out with the same women (or men).

Pam was slightly different though. She had not grown up in the Victorian town that looked out over one of the prettiest coastlines in Britain. She had been just another holidaymaker when she had visited the town in the early 1980s. But the moment she set eyes on Paul she had known she wanted to be with him – and now Sidmouth was her only home.

But, not being a local had its compensations. It meant that people were more curious about Pam. She had a certain mystique about her and she spoke with a much posher accent than her rough and tumble West Country husband. Many of her neighbours had been really impressed when they heard Pam had been at an

23

expensive private school. In fact she had even been a prefect. But Paul had put all that high class nonsense firmly behind her. She was his wife now – and he didn't want to even think about the rich and exclusive world she came from.

He didn't like all that sort of talk one bit. Some of his friends reckoned it was because he had a chip on his shoulder about being 'common.' Paul just insisted all that 'rich folk talk' got on his nerves.

Like any reasonably attractive woman, Pam enjoyed flattery and attention. It was nice to be appreciated. Unfortunately, she rarely had an opportunity to meet that many new friends these days. That made her visit to *Carinas* all the more enjoyable. She was actually able to come into contact with other people.

She had specially washed and ironed her favourite white dress for that evening. It was not often she had the chance to wear it. As she sipped slowly on her own non-alcoholic drink, she was aware of occasional looks from some of the men who passed by their table. At first, she did not look up as she felt a touch embarrassed. But there seemed to be so many single men out there.

Across the table, Paul was studying the women in much the same way the men were examining his wife. Some of them looked really cracking, he thought to himself. If only I was single again. Paul especially liked the ones in their early twenties who tended to favour short, skin tight skirts combined with dangerously high stiletto heeled shoes. A new one seemed to drift past his table every other second. Where did all this talent come from?

Ironically, it was only when the numbers of single, pretty girls started to disperse that Paul noticed a man standing nearby leaning against a pillar ever so casually. He seemed to be looking over this way. But then again perhaps he wasn't.

For a few moments, Paul ignored the man. But when he glanced back in his direction he was still there. What was he looking at? Paul turned to face his wife and momentarily caught sight of her eyes. They were definitely pointed in the direction of that man. What the hell was happening?

Pam had only given the man the briefest of glances after she had felt his gaze penetrating her. He was quite a good looking fellow but that was irrelevant. She wondered if perhaps he was a friend of Paul's. It was only natural that she should respond for a split second. But it was at that precise moment, Paul caught her looking at the other man.

'Why are you looking at that man? Do you know him?'

Paul sounded agitated.

Pam was taken aback. She was lost for words.

'You know him don't you?' he said

Paul was convincing himself there was a reason behind his wife's glance at that man.

'Don't be silly. I thought he was a friend of yours.'

Paul took another huge gulp of his lager and then got up. Pam was puzzled. No. Surely he wouldn't. But he did. At that moment, he swayed, slightly drunkenly over towards the man.

'Hey. Why are you looking at my wife? Take your bloody eyes off her.'

Pam was now deeply embarrassed. She could not believe Paul would do such a thing. The other man said nothing and tried to walk away. But Paul was having

25

none of it. Pam had seen this happen so many times before. Why couldn't her husband control his obsessive jealousy?

'Come on you. Out with it. How well do you know her?'

Pam and Paul's friends were now fidgeting nervously. They'd seen it all before. But no-one got up to do something about his behaviour. Everybody at that table knew how violent Paul could be. None of them wanted to take him on. But, ultimately, it was Pam who would have to take some sort of action – and she would pay dearly for it later.

'Don't be so daft Paul. I've never seen him before in my life.'

'Liar. Fucking liar. I bet you've shagged him proper!'

'That's enough Paul. Come on. Home. This is ridiculous.'

'I told you woman. Don't use those long words on me. Don't try and make me feel common.'

As the stranger disappeared into the crowded dance floor, Paul struggled to free himself of his wife's grasp. He hadn't finished his entertainment for that night by any means.

'You fucking slut. How dare you . . .'

The crunching sound of his fist sinking into her cheek was horrendous. Pam felt her teeth wobble as he connected with her face.

She crumpled to the floor, desperately holding her chin in place with her left hand. Too stunned to move. Too frightened to breath. Too terrified to utter a word. Then she heard it coming. A whoosh of air as his right hobnailed boot smashed straight into her shin as she lay there still trying to recover from his first flurry of punches. The crack was so loud it might well have broken the bone.

'Get your fucking clothes off you whore. You're just like a dog.'

That word 'dog' filled Pam with more pain and fear than the physical assault that had just occurred. It meant only one thing. He was going to degrade her like he had done so often before. She really did not know if she could take it again.

'Come on. Get those fucking clothes off *now*'

Pam's favourite white dress that she had so lovingly washed and pressed just a few hours earlier was now ripped down the front exposing one of her breasts – brutally uncovered by her monster husband.

He walked over to the wardrobe next to their bed. It could mean only one thing. She felt the dread of expectation sinking through her mind and body. She knew the worst was still to come.

She had no choice. She was a prisoner in that bedroom yet again. She would have to do as he ordered. She had no option.

'I want everything off. Everything.'

Pam felt like a scared fox being pursued by one large, brutal hound. She scrambled along the floor and into the corner of the room and tried to sit up against the wall. But the pain was so severe, she could hardly move the leg he had so callously kicked just moments earlier. There was no escape.

Pam had already started to give up. She was going to surrender once again. She started to remove her dress. In the end it was easier to rip it off. It took less time – that meant he would get it all over more quickly.

But getting her panties off was more difficult. Every time she tried to half get up to pull them off, she felt overcome by dizziness. But Paul Sainsbury was in no mood to be patient. His animalistic urges were taking full priority. He looked down at the pathetic creature who was his wife and grabbed one of her ankles before yanking the panties off. She could smell the awful stench of stale lager wafting from his lips. His eyes looked almost dead with alcohol as he staggered back to the wardrobe and pulled out various items.

'Come on dog. Come on. Behave like a dog. Be treated like one. You love it don't you? Don't you?'

Pam knew her husband was expecting her to reply. But her jaw and cheekbone were still vibrating from the throbbing pain inflicted by his punches minutes before.

'Come on. Say it. You dog.'

Pam looked up pathetically towards her towering brute of a husband.

'Woof. Woof.'

She could hardly spit the words out the hurt was so bad. But Paul was satisfied . . . for the moment at least. He had lots more plans in store for his wife.

'Don't get up dog. I am going to take you for walkies.'

Paul then produced from behind his back a collar and lead. Pam had seen it all before. She knew what to expect as he leant down and fixed the studded choker around her neck.

'You're a bitch and I am going to teach you a lesson. Dogs need training.'

Pam's brain was so scrambled by the onslaught that she had all but given up. That was the way he liked it. She just accepted her punishment – and provided him with the pleasure he so sickly craved.

Now she was on all fours being led around the bedroom by the lead. Every time she slowed down, he pulled viciously at the choker. She could feel her throat being pulled in. It was a bit like the sensation of drowning. She would snatch a few breaths and then he would yank viciously at the collar causing her neck to wrench.

Her husband had also now stripped naked. But he had only just begun. He was about to force his wife to perform some of the most degrading sex acts imaginable but first he wanted to make absolutely sure she really did feel like a dog.

'Come on eat. Eat I said.'

Paul Sainsbury put the dog bowl down on the floor by his wife's head. She did not know what was in the bowl. But just the smell of it made her feel nauseous. It could have been anything but it looked awful. Brown, splodgy pieces of something that filled the entire beige coloured bowl.

'Eat. I said Eat.'

Pam crooked her neck downwards towards the bowl. She had no choice. If she did not eat it, he would beat her until she did. She may as well get it all over and done with as quickly as possible. This was a regularly recurring nightmare in the sad life of Pamela Sainsbury.

As her tongue probed the dark mess just in front of her tear swollen eyes, she shut her mind out and began to eat.

* * *

Two hours had passed since that first punch. Now, at last, he had collapsed on the bed in a drunken stupor.

She had endured pain and penetration in virtually every orifice in her body. The spirit had been drained out of her but the frustration she was feeling was building up.

Pam struggled to get up off the floor. She fell back down at first. The dizziness brought on by her beating was so severe she could hardly balance herself. His cruelty towards her had known no bounds. She felt as if she had been raped, tortured and sodomised by a brutal attacker – not her own husband.

But through that haze of horror she felt a deep anger from within. Never again. Never again. Never again.

As she pulled at the leather studded choker that was still tightly wrapped around her neck, she felt a surge of disgust, fury and contempt for that animal lying there just a few feet away.

Throwing the collar and lead across the bedroom, she put on her dressing gown and sat for a few moments at the end of their double bed. This had happened over and over again. How could she just let him carry on? How many more times would she allow him to turn sex from an act of love into an act of aggression? Pamela Sainsbury had finally snapped. She was going to do something about it.

She washed her face and tried to straighten out her bedraggled appearance. Now was the time. She went to the tool cupboard at the bottom of the stairs of their modest three-bedroomed council house. She found Paul's work tool bag. In it was a long length of plumb line.

*   *   *

Back in the bedroom, Pam stopped and looked at the snoring hulk of a man who lay in their bed. He seemed so peaceful lying there. She had to make herself remember the disgusting degradation he had just put her through. This was the time to act. After eight years of abuse it had to be stopped.

Pam tied one end of the plumb line onto the head-board of their bed. Then she carefully and gently wrapped the rope fully around her husband's neck. He still couldn't feel a thing. The line was not tight – yet. He stirred at that moment. She thought perhaps she had disturbed him but it was only the restless sleep of a man pickled in alcohol.

Pam tightly wrapped both her small hands around the rope as if she were about to pull in a tug of war. She stood by the side of the bed with the rope coming towards her from her husband's neck. She took one last glance at his face. He was the man she had given up her entire life to be with. The man she had produced a family with. The man who actually probably really did love her in his own twisted, perverted way.

For a moment, she wondered if this really was the right thing to do. Perhaps he would change? Maybe there was a chance they could start all over again?

Pam knew there and then that would never happen. She had been through all this before. He had made promises and broken them all immediately. He wanted to love her to death. Now she had to kill him to avoid her own demise. There was no choice. With one huge

31

heave, she pulled frantically at the rope. She could feel the strain on the headboard. It creaked as she tightened her grip. She also felt the rope burning into her palms as she pulled with all her strength.

Then he woke up. The very thing she most dreaded. He had shaken out of his drunken slumber as the rope dug deeply into his windpipe. She saw his eyes upon her. They were appealing, terrified eyes. The exact same look she had given him so often during the course of her beatings and abuse. Now he was suffering. He was experiencing the terror and the fear.

The moment his eyes opened she pulled even harder on the rope. It was as if his sheer agony was inciting her to accelerate the process of death. She could not stop herself now.

The colour was draining out of his face rapidly. She could see the pupils of his eyes begin to dilate. His fingers had long since given up trying to grasp the rope away from his neck. His hands and arms had flopped down by the side of the bed. Pam somehow seemed to have found even more inner strength. The power she was generating was increasing. Nothing would allow her to let go of that rope until her job was complete.

The burning sensation caused by the rope digging into her hands had been replaced by deep set cuts in her skin. But she did not flinch. The pupils of his eyes had now completely dilated. There was just a flickering of white, nothing else. The eyelids were wide open though. It was as if they had been jammed open by some exterior force. Pam was glad his eyes were still open. It meant he had seen everything until the bitter end. That was important. That suffering had to continue for as long as possible.

With one last surge of energy, Pam gave one final tug.

But it was clear her husband was already well and truly dead. She relaxed her grip. Then his body seemed to convulse. Perhaps he was still alive? Maybe she had not completed the death sentence?

It seemed like an electric shock was running through his body for a split second. Pam was startled. She tried to regain her grip on that rope again. But by the time she had pulled it tight once more, her husband's body was still and limp. There was no life left inside him.

Now she had to remove him from the bed. He had bludgeoned her body and mind for the last time. She had to be practical for a moment. She did not want her children, Lindsay and Terry to find their father like this.

Then Pam looked over at that wardrobe. It had become like an evil dungeon where he kept the whips, the collars, the leads and the other awful, perverted equipment that he had forced her to wear over the previous eight years.

Yes. He belonged in the wardrobe. There amongst the sick strands of leather and studs. Pam would make sure he was very comfortable there.

She untied the rope from the bed head and then noticed how deeply cut her hands had become. She went to wash down her hands before preparing to haul that dead piece of meat across the bedroom floor.

By the time she managed to push his body into that wardrobe, it was almost 3am. But it could have been any time of the day or night to Pam. She was caught up in the web of a fantasy that had become a reality. Had she really just killed her husband? Did she actually strangle the life out of him? Then, as if looking for some kind of reassurance, she glanced at the calendar by the side of their double bed – the bed where it had all just happened. And she wrote, words that soothed her tortured self, justified her actions, made sense of what had happened:

THIS IS THE FIRST DAY
OF THE REST OF MY LIFE.

It was September 1, 1990 and Pamela Sainsbury's life had in fact begun all over again.

'He beat me up last night. Almost broke my leg. I told him to get out otherwise I'd call the police.'

Pam was very convincing as she told one of her husband's relatives why he was not at home.

'I think he's gone up north. I don't care anyway. I never want to see him ever again.' Only she realised that fact had already been guaranteed. None of the Sainsbury family or friends seemed that surprised. Some of them had witnessed his awful fit of jealousy at *Carinas* Nightclub a few days earlier. Paul was a brutal sort. Good riddance.

But while Paul Sainsbury had definitely gone for ever, he still presented something of a problem for his wife. Where could she put his body?

It was four days since his death and his lifeless remains were still stuffed in amongst his sex manuals and bondage equipment.

Pam decided that she had to do something. And once again, she was on her own. She could not afford to risk telling anyone.

* * *

Pam made one last check to see if the children were fast asleep. She crept into their bedroom and looked at their angelic faces for a few moments. It reassured her that all the horrors she had suffered had been worthwhile. Just to see them soundly sleeping was enough to convince her she had done the right thing. They were her flesh and blood and she wanted them to have the happiest lives possible. She would make sure of that.

Now that the house was quiet, she had to sort out the problem of Paul. She had to dispose of that body. But how? He was simply too heavy to carry out of the house in one piece. Pam removed a one foot long tenon saw and a razor sharp carving knife from the kitchen and took them upstairs. She braced herself as she went to open the wardrobe – that evil mini-dungeon of horrors had got its just dessert now. The Master. The animal who inflicted such pain and anguish on Pam was now rotting amongst his own perverted possessions.

His stiff corpse fell out into the bedroom as she unlocked the double doors. The stench of death wafted out that instant. His naked body had turned a bluey-grey colour.

Pam held her breath for a moment. Some of the contents of his seized up bowels were still in that wardrobe. It was a grisly sight for anyone to suffer. But Pam quickly recovered her composure. She had a job of work to do. She was not going to let him beat her – even in death. She would never again allow him the satisfaction of appalling her. She wanted to get away with the killing. She wanted to free herself from his evil spell. He was not going to force her into submission now – or ever again.

Pam rolled the heavy corpse of her husband over onto

35

some plastic sheeting she had laid out on the floor of the bedroom. It was time to begin.

At first, it seemed really difficult to saw the arm at the shoulder blade. The instrument just did not want to embed itself in the skin. Then Pam pressed down hard so that the razor sharp instrument sliced a niche in the soft bluey flesh. At last she could really get going.

Once she had conquered a certain technique with regard to the sawing, it was all relatively easy. Within a minute or two, the arm had been almost separated from the rest of the body. Pam gave it a slight tug and heard the final strands of flesh tearing as she pulled it off and lay it in a black dustbin liner. The only thing that surprised her was the weight. It was heavy. There was no way one could gingerly remove it. It definitely required a certain amount of strength and that made the whole process feel ever more real and graphic. Pam had envisaged it being much easier.

After depositing both arms in the plastic bag alongside the body, she moved down the corpse to begin work on the legs. They were even harder. Initially, she tried to cut them from where the thighs meet the stomach but that proved impossible. With a heave, she rolled the body over and began slicing through the hip bone.

More than an hour later, Pam had completed removing the the arms and legs from the torso. But there was still the matter of the head. She looked down at the cold, lifeless form on her bedroom floor and wondered if it really was Paul. Maybe he would come walking through that door at any moment? She sat crouched there on the plastic sheeting alongside what remained of her husband in a sort of trance.

How can I be sure? How can I be certain he really is dead if I dispose of the body?

These questions were really troubling Pam. So long as his body had been rotting in that wardrobe she felt reassured that he was definitely dead. But now she was about to get rid of the body for ever. There would be nothing left of Paul – nothing to show her he really was dead.

She lent down and started to saw through his neck. By the time she had separated the head from the torso she had decided: she was going to keep his head. She wanted to always be absolutely sure he was actually dead.

It was way past midnight by the time Pam had hauled the two huge dustbin bags down to the back door. She hoped no-one would see her when she began digging a hole near the vegetable patch at the end of the garden.

She took a shovel out of the garden shed and found what looked like a suitable spot and began digging. Well, she tried to dig. But the ground was as hard as a rock. There had been little rain for weeks and the earth was solid. No matter how much she crashed that shovel into the ground, only a few small clumps of earth moved.

She tried another part of the garden but it was much the same story. There was no way she could dig holes deep enough to bury those bags. Now she was getting worried that the neighbours in Le Locle Close might see her out in the garden late at night and begin to wonder. No-one had stirred yet. But if she made much more noise they were certain to get disturbed and then they would see what she was up to.

Pam returned to the kitchen, distraught. The remains of her husband in those two plastic bags were just sitting there by the back door. *You can't get rid of me*, they said in Paul's mocking voice, *I've beaten you*.

What could she do? He was not going to win. He just couldn't! She would think of another way of disposal.

Pam walked back down to the bottom of the garden and pushed her husband's wheelbarrow towards the back door. She struggled to load one bag at a time onto the wheelbarrow. The tension and turmoil of the previous few days was catching up with her. But any weakness was overcome when she thought about the driving force behind her actions. The quest to start a new life. That was enough to keep her going.

Pam was about to take an enormous risk but she had to get rid of the body. She weaved her way down the path to the back wall and ground to a halt. Then she summoned all her strength to heave the bag over the wall and into the the bushes that backed onto their house. It was thick bracken and a hedge that belonged to a field that never seemed to be used for anything in particular.

Pam repeated the operation with the next body bag. She had got rid of the body the best way she could. She had got it off the premises – that was the most important thing.

Back in the kitchen, there was one bag remaining. It was smaller than the others. Round. Shaped like a large football. That would stay at home, with pride of place in her cupboard, a perpetual reminder that he would not, could not, return.

* * *

The music was throbbing away as usual in *Carinas* Nightclub. But there was one big difference for Pamela Sainsbury. She was not living in fear of a severe beating the moment she got home.

For this was her first visit without her husband to the nightspot that marked the beginning and the end of her eight years of horror at the hands of a monster. As she relaxed near the busy bar with a girlfriend, she reflected on how – just a few weeks earlier – her life had all been so different.

She had stuck rigidly to that promise she made to herself the night Paul died. Every day she would look at the words written on her calendar: THIS IS THE FIRST DAY OF THE REST OF MY LIFE.

Now she was living the rest of that life and it was proving far more enjoyable than she would ever have believed. She could even afford to laugh and smile at men who caught her eye across the dance floor without facing that inevitable degradation. Soon she would feel confident enough to start going out with men again. Enjoying the company of, hopefully, gentler males than the sicko she had married.

But to start with she would keep them all at a bit of distance. It was going to take time to adjust back into the real world. For not only had she faced brutality beyond belief at the hands of Paul, but he had also forced her to spend most of her time trapped in that tiny house in much the same way the hostages were kept locked up in faceless parts of Beruit. She needed to adjust to normal, decent, hard-working people. But her girl friends were proving a real mainstay.

They felt sorry for Pam. Abandoned by her bullying husband, she had been left to bring up the kids alone. She deserved to get out and have some fun occasionally.

By the time Pam and her friends left *Carinas*, they felt she was well on the road to recovery. But there was something nagging at her. A feeling that perhaps, just perhaps *he* was still around. Still watching over her. Still waiting for her to get home so he could batter her once again. Everywhere she looked there were reminders of him. This was his home town after all. It was an awful feeling. Just the slightest chance that he might not be dead. It sent a shiver of fear through her body.

There was only one solution. The moment Pam got home that evening she rushed through the hallway and pulled open the door to the tiny meter cupboard under the stairs.

It was OK. There was the shape of his head pressing through the plastic bags she had tightly wrapped around it. She knew then that he was definitely dead. She had to keep his head as a constant reminder of her freedom. She stood there in the darkened hall for a few seconds and just stared straight at the grisly stump. She knew that no-one must know what bizarre lengths she had gone to. But just so long as she knew, then it would be alright.

As the months passed by, Pamela gradually rediscovered her life once more. She learnt to enjoy herself. She started to date other men. She became a happier, more content person. And everytime, she felt any doubts or guilt about what she had done, she would return to that meter cupboard and make sure he was still there. The only really distressing aspect that still remained was the seclusion she felt whenever she faced his head there under the stairs. It was the only time she felt all alone in the world. She so desperately wanted to tell someone what had happened. Supressing the truth was not easy. There had been many times over the previous months when she had sat down in the kitchen of that same house – just a few feet from where Paul's lifeless face stood in the darkness – with a girlfriend and wondered to herself if she should talk about what happened on that awful night. Each time, she would hold herself back at the last moment, suddenly aware that it would be crazy to expect anyone not to tell the authorities.

But by the summer of 1991, Pam was reaching breaking point. She had to tell someone. She could not bottle it up any longer. She had managed to convince herself that by admitting it all to a friend it would then wipe out any of the remaining g ilt once and for all. They say confession wipes the slate clean. Pam believed that her new life was perfect in all but one respect. It was time to tell.

'I am so relieved I've told you. It's so good to tell someone.'

Pam's girlfriend did not know how to respond. She was shocked and horrified by what she had just been told. Unfortunately for Pam, she had chosen the wrong friend to confide in.

'We'd like to talk to you about your missing husband.'

The uniformed policeman standing on the front door of Pam's house seemed gentle enough in his approach. But she knew why he was there.

'Just give me a few minutes. I need to organise a babysitter for the kids.'

The officer was happy to wait while Pam went back inside the house. It gave Pam a chance to seek reassurance just one more time. She opened that meter cupboard door for the last time and looked in at him. It was enough. She knew for sure he was dead. He would never return. Now she felt a sense of relief that the police had come. It was perhaps the missing piece of the jigsaw. The one aspect that weighed on her mind. She had to confess to guarantee he never came back. Now the police were there she knew for certain he had gone. Calmly, she lifted the head of her dead husband and dropped it into her rubbish bin for the dustmen to take the next morning . . .

On Friday, December 14, 1991, Pamela Sainsbury was placed on two years probation after admitting the manslaughter of her husband Paul. She also pleaded guilty to a second charge of obstructing the coroner in his duty by concealing the body.

Plymouth Crown Court judge Mr Justice Auld told her: 'For many years you suffered regular and increasing violence and other forms of extreme sadism and sexual degradation at his hands. There is no right sentence in a case such as this. On one hand it is my duty to mark the serious crime of manslaughter which you have committed. However, I am prepared in the exceptional circumstances of this case to make a probation order for two years.'

The head of Paul Sainsbury was never recovered by police.

Bambi

Even in her jogging pants Lawrencia Bembenek looked stunning. Everything about her was just right. Her face was beautifully structured. Her flowing chestnut-brown hair styled perfectly. Her breasts firm and ample but not too large. Her bottom curved, yet delicate. The perfect all-American 22-year old dream.

But it was her eyes, her eyes that really clinched it. Huge dark brown seas of sensuality. Always wide open. Always happy. Always looking straight at you. Like the eyes of tentative deer. They had it all and they landed Lawrencia with a nickname that was going to stick for the rest of her life – Bambi. Somehow it summed her up. She had an endearing air of innocence about her, a vulnerability that was incredibly attractive. But there was also an animal cunning – a natural instinct to survive.

She certainly had an extraordinary effect on policeman Fred Schultz. He had met Bambi just a few days earlier at a bar in their home town of Milwaukee. They had struck up a brief and pleasant enough conversation – but no more. Bambi was no easy pick-up for recently divorced older men like Schultz. She did not mind talking to him but that was as far as it would go.

'How about coming jogging with me tomorrow?'

Bambi was taken aback. She had been expecting all the usual lines about coming back to my place but this guy was asking her for a jog. That shy, somewhat icy veneer had been knocked off balance. This was not what she expected. Maybe this guy was genuine?

'Sure. Why not? What time do you want to meet?'

Bambi could not believe herself. What was she doing agreeing to go for a jog with a man she did not even know? But there was something about him. He seemed honest. He seemed to really care. In any case, he could hardly attack her while they were jogging.

So they agreed to a date – *If* that is the way to describe running on the streets of Milwaukee. It was hardly a romantic setting for two would be lovers, but it seemed appropriate at the time.

The actual jogging part of that first meeting was not exactly informative. As they huffed and puffed their way around a vast park on the edge of the city, there was little energy left for actual conversation. That would come later. For now they were testing each other's physical limitations without even touching. And Bambi was proving the fitter of the two.

She soon found herself racing yards ahead of the 32-year old detective. But he did not care one tiny bit. Being beaten by a woman did not bother Fred Schultz. He was enjoying a completely different aspect of their race through the park. He loved watching her slim and shapely body movements ahead of him. Her buttocks seemed so firm through the skin tight material of her figure-hugging sweat pants.

Fred reckoned he could pant behind that body for the rest of his life. And maybe beyond.

When they finally came to a halt, he could not take his eyes off her hot, glistening face. Watching the beads of sweat gently roll down her forehead, past those gorgeous eyes onto the perfectly formed cheeks then cascading onto those moist lips before her tongue darted out and licked them away.

Fred Schultz was smitten. He did not even know her full name yet. But this had to be the woman for him. She just had to be.

Then it happened. That spark of coincidence that marks the start of any successful relationship. As Bambi and Fred sat down in a café to chat she asked him that classic question.

'What do you do Fred?'

'Oh. I'm a cop. What's your line?'

Bambi stopped in her tracks. For a moment Fred thought it was that old familiar sign of a woman who doesn't like cops. Maybe her father's in jail? Perhaps she's had a run in with the police? It happened so often he just took it for granted. He had hoped and prayed this woman might be different but now it seemed that he was facing the usual anti-police sentiments.

But just the opposite was true.

She sipped her coffee, licked the froth away with her tongue and smiled. 'I used to be a cop too.'

And with those words, Bambi instantly sealed the fate of a relationship that would lead to marriage and so much more besides.

The wedding was a simple affair. They had little money but it cost nothing to choose the most romantic date of the year for the ceremony – Valentine's Day, 1981.

45

Fred had been married before. With an ex-wife Christine and two sons to support, he did not have a lot of spare change at the end of each month. The $363.50 mortgage plus $330 in child support soaked up almost half his detective's take-home salary. It was tough. And Bambi wasn't in the big earnings league either. Working as an aerobics instructor by day and a Playboy Bunny by night, she was struggling to pay off mounting debts.

But they had each other – and that was what mattered most.

Bambi regularly blew her lid about the money Fred was shelling out to Christine and the kids. Here she was marrying an older, successful man but they could hardly afford the rent on a modest one-bedroomed apartment while Christine lived a few blocks away in a lovely detached house. It just did not seem right. But Fred had obligations to keep – and he was a man of his word.

Still, it continued to really grate at Bambi. She could not get it out of her head. Even as they hosted a special gathering of close friends at a dinner party on the evening of the wedding, her mind kept wandering back to it.

'You know. It would pay to have Christine blown away.'

Judy Zess stopped chewing the piece of a chicken in her mouth for a moment. She could not believe what she just heard her old friend and former room-mate Bambi say.

This was the eve of her wedding and she was threatening to 'blow away' her new husband's first wife. What on earth did she mean? It was hardly a healthy start to the marriage. Judy Zess never forgot those few, sinister words. They would one day have a prophetic significance.

Fred Schultz, however, was deliriously happy. He had found himself a beautiful bride to restart his life with. After years of marital grief with Christine, he truly believed he had found the girl of his dreams. Someone he could spend forever with.

He was so besotted, he ignored the sneers of some of his colleagues at work. They remembered Bambi as someone quite different from the pretty, sensual creature he had fallen in love with. They recalled her as being the 'dope head' girl cop who did not charge a pal when she was caught smoking cannabis. In their eyes, she was trouble – and she had shamed her unit by sympathising with druggies. In fact, they suspected she even smoked marijuana herself. That was one of the reasons they fired her back in 1980.

Bambi had a lot of enemies inside the Milwaukee Police Department:

'She was too darned pretty to be a cop in the first place.'

'Her type should never have joined the force.'

Bambi certainly provoked opinions. She was a person of extremes after all. You either loved her or hated her and Schultz loved her to death. But his fellow colleagues hated her with a vengeance.

Nevertheless, there was one aspect of Bambi that her husband deeply detested – her job at the local Playboy Club. Fred did not care that on a good couple of nights, Bambi could earn the entire month's rent on their modest apartment. He may have been permanently broke but no wife of his was going to work in *that* place.

Bambi sort of understood her new husband's feelings but she also knew they were financially hard pressed. In any case, she had a great body. Why not show if off a little and get paid for the pleasure?

'Those guys pay me a $50 tip just so they can look at my body.' Bambi was very matter of fact about it. She would never, ever even consider selling her body for sex. But dressing up in a slinky leotard with a fake bunny tail stuck on her bottom did not seem so bad. In any case, she was proud of her fit, lean body. She knew she had good breasts and gorgeous hips. She did not mind wiggling the right parts if necessary. It was all harmless stuff.

But Fred was adamant. He did not like the idea of all those guys lusting after her – and it was hardly the right sort of career for a policeman's wife. So, after much cajoling, Bambi handed in her bunny's tail and waved goodbye to those, sleazy, risky nights at the Playboy Club. The trouble was that it gave her more time to herself. More time to think. More time to brood. More time to get angry. More time to get vicious.

Fred was working longer and longer hours in his job as a busy crime detective on the streets of Milwaukee. Crime was rife in most neighbourhoods in that gritty, busy city. And that meant Fred and his colleagues really had their work cut out for them.

It also meant a lot of lonely nights at home in front of the television set for Bambi. She could not concentrate on most programmes. Her thoughts were filled with vengeance. Here she was in this tiny, cramped apartment while *that woman* had a beautiful house. Why? Why was Bambi suffering when she was the one who had just got married?

The only TV shows that diverted her attention were the bleak crime movies. The grisly murders that keep viewers gripped to their seats in terror. They did not scare Bambi. They just made her start to wonder . . .

The evening of May 27, 1981, was hot and steamy in Milwaukee. But that did not affect Christine Schultz and her two sons Sean, 11, and Shannon, 7. The children were comfortably tucked up in the air conditioned bedroom of the family's well-maintained detached home in one of the city's better Southside suburbs.

As 30-year old Christine kissed them gently goodnight and left the bedroom, her thoughts could not have been further from the happiness of her ex-husband and his new, young wife. She could only recall the unhappy years with Fred. The arguing. The fighting. The tears. Now, at last she could get on with her new life. A new lover and even the chance of a fresh, happier marriage eventually.

She watched her boys as they drifted into sleep. Life would come good for them, she was sure of it. A thunderous roar broke overhead as a huge airliner made its descent to the nearby airport at Mitchell Field, but they slept through it, safe in a cocoon of dreams.

Christine quietly tip-toed out of their room and headed towards the bedroom she once shared with Fred. A peaceful night in front of the television. She could think of nothing nicer.

Settled into the comfy double divan, she propped herself up with three pillows and immersed herself in one of her favourite shows – M*A*S*H*. Christine laughed out loud at the hilarious adventures of Radar and all the rest of the gang who starred in the top rating programme. She loved the show's harsh, cynical humour. The reality of it appealed to her. But the real world outside was about to swallow her up forever.

It was 2.20am when little Sean stirred from his deep slumber. At first he thought he was dreaming. He could feel something cold, almost damp, pressing over his face and mouth. Then he felt a choking sensation as if a cord were tightening around his neck.

This was no dream. This was the ultimate nightmare. For a split second, he kept his eyes tightly closed. Hoping that if he did so then it would all go away. But he was having trouble breathing now and his throat felt as if it were about to explode. He had to open his eyes. There was no other possible means of escape.

So he did, and there was terror in its truest form. No goblins, no wicked witches, no make-believe video that sent shivers down your spine but you could laugh at later. Just a leather gloved hand clasping, pressing down on his face. Then another hand, fumbling for a second then pulling a cord tight around his neck. Sean's first scream was muffled. Then his assailant loosened the pressure momentarily so that the noose around his neck could be pulled even tighter.

Just one more breath Sean told himself as his world began to go blurry at the edges through lack of oxygen. He let out an ear-piercing shriek. It was his only chance.

His last one. Sean put his entire little body and spirit into that yell and it had the desired effect. The intruder ran out of the room.

What was happening?

The two boys lay there too afraid to move at first. They just did not know what to do. Maybe they should just go back to sleep and then they would wake up in the morning to find it never really happened?

Boom. Boom.

It sounded like a firecracker going off in their mother's bedroom. The boys froze with fear. The reality of that attack moments earlier had now dawned on them utterly and completely. They ran to the bedroom. The bedroom where once they had rushed to sleep with their mother and father whenever they had a bad dream. Now they were about to encounter the worst type of nightmare – reality.

But their protective instincts towards their mother were paramount in their minds at that moment. As they dashed across the hallway they encountered the worst piece of evidence imaginable as a tall, shadowy figure pushed past them towards the stairs and the front door.

They found her face down on the bed. A sight no person should ever have to witness, let alone two small children. There in that bedroom they faced the aftermath of murder – and the victim was their mother.

A clothesline was tied around one hand. She had obviously put up a struggle. In her right shoulder was a gaping gunshot wound, flesh ripped away to the bone. But it was the blue bandanna gagging her mouth that was the most startling sight. It seemed to contort her face into a thousand lines of fear. Thankfully, her eyes were closed so neither of those innocent children had to see the horror etched permanently within.

But how can a child react to such a horrendous scene? They are not emotionally mature enough to know how to cope. Why should they be prepared by their parents for such a terrifying situation? No-one expects it to happen to them.

Sean aged ten years in those first few seconds as he stood in front of his mother's bloodied body. He tried desperately to stop the blood spreading from Christine's shoulder wound. Thank goodness he did not try to move her body because then he would have seen the full extent of that wound – caused by a single .38 bullet shot at point blank range in her back. It had glanced off her shoulder blade and gone through her heart. She never stood a chance. But it was better this way. At least Sean did not have to look at the graphic nature of the bullet's journey through his mother's body.

As Shannon stood by watching in a terrified trance, Sean struggled vainly to stop the blood from draining out of Christine's body. So often she had been the one to dab his cuts and bruises. She had kissed them better when they hurt like hell. She had covered the cuts with plaster to stop them dripping blood. She had loved and cared for him whatever the circumstances.

Now he was bravely trying to return the previous eleven years of love and attention. But no matter how hard he tried, there was nothing he could do to save her. There was no ebbing life to preserve. She had gone before they even reached the room.

A few minutes later, the shaking, quivering youngster

called his mother's boyfriend, policeman Stu Honeck, who lived around the corner.

The cops arrived within minutes.

'It's just not fair Mike. I can hardly afford the price of a pair of shoes.'

Fred Schultz was complaining to his partner, Det Michael Durfee, about that alimony yet again. Day in day out, the same old story. It was getting too much.

They were filing a burglary report when Fred picked up the ringing phone at their desk. Within moments, his face went white. His eyes began to well up with tears and then he dropped the telephone and left it hanging there.

Fred had just been told that his ex-wife – the mother of his two young sons – had been brutally murdered. He was in a daze. He did not know what to do. He just sat there slumped on his desk, his head in his hands sobbing. There was nothing his partner or anyone else could say. But he did have Bambi to turn to. She was still there. She would support him. She would help him cope. He had to turn to some-body.

Peep. Peep. Peep. Peep . . .

The line at their home was engaged. What was Bambi doing on the telephone at 2.40 in the morning? Fred was puzzled. He needed her support. Her love. And she was on the phone. Why?

Finally he got through.

'Laurie, wake up! Chris has been shot. She's dead. I'll call you back when I can.'

Bambi said later she thought it was all a dream when

53

Fred called her. But in fact, she was the instigator of the worst nightmare of all.

'He was a big guy with browny red type of hair and a pony tail.'

Sean had somehow regained enough composure to describe to detectives what the intruder looked like – less than an hour after the awful incident occurred.

The youngster told them he was wearing a baggy, green army jacket and black, police-type shoes. And a green jogging suit. And the gun, the gun had a silver pearl handle.

At least the detectives had something to go on.

'I'm sorry Fred but I got to see if your gun has been fired recently.'

Fred Schultz was stunned. His ex-wife had been murdered just a few hours earlier and now his partner Mike Durfee was at his front door suggesting that his own gun might have been used in the killing.

'What the fuck is this?' he screamed.

Mike gulped, he had to do it – but the despair on his friend's face . . .

All he could manage in response was, 'it's just a formality.'

Bambi watched coolly as her husband and his partner carefully checked the gun. Durfee found dust on the hammer and sniffed for any tell-tale signs of gunpowder odour. There was nothing. This weapon had not been used for quite some time.

'Look Fred. What can I say? It had to be checked.'

Fred nodded slowly. Deep down, he understood the reasons behind his partner's visit. In fact, he felt fairly relieved because he knew who they would all be pointing the finger of suspicion at – his beautiful new young wife.

Bambi did not bat an eyelid. She looked as sexy and seductive as ever when they finally climbed into bed together to try and snatch a few hours sleep.

Policemen have a well known coldness when it comes to death. They encounter it so frequently that they soon become emotionally divorced from the reality of all the normal responses it provokes.

'It's just a body. It's not someone you know and love so it means nothing.'

An everyday occurrence. If it starts getting to you it's time to get out. But sometimes, inevitably, there are occasions when it hits home. The death of Christine Schultz should have been one of those occasions. Yet, bizarrely, Fred had recovered his composure completely by the time he was summoned to the city morgue to formally identify his ex-wife's body.

The cop and his pretty young ex-cop wife walked into the cold, sterile room as if they had been there a thousand times before. And they had. But surely this time it was different? They were about to see the brutally slain corpse of the woman who bore him two children. It had to be a difficult moment for any person – surely?

'Hey Laurie look at the size of this wound will you?'

Bambi was astonished. Whatever her true feelings towards the woman who lay on that morgue slab, she hardly felt in the mood to start passing medical comments on the size of the wounds.

But Fred was insistent.

'Come on Laurie. You saw enough stiffs when you were in the force.' As it happened Bambi had not been 'in the force' for very long and she managed to avoid seeing too many 'stiffs'. But that was irrelevant. She felt reluctant to go near that corpse. She did not want to face the reality of the situation. It frightened her.

Still Fred persisted. For a good few minutes he stood examining the fatal wound that had rubbed out his ex-wife's life.

'Wow! That's some wound.'

Bambi could not take this gruesome verbal post mortem another moment longer. She left Fred alone with his ex-wife for the one and only time.

Cops investigating Christine's tragic slaying were baffled. All their enquiries kept leading them to Bambi. She had told so many people of her dislike for Christine. The threats were common place, the envy an open secret. But so far they had not a shred of evidence.

Even Fred began to wonder. He took a pretty active role in the investigation. Some of his more cynical colleagues suggested it was to hide his own guilt. But it was becoming more and more apparent to Fred that Bambi certainly had the motive, if not the means.

There were no witnesses to place Bambi outside of that apartment on that night in May. But she had access to the off-duty gun Fred kept at home and the keys to the house where his ex-wife lived. There was no sign of forced entry by the murderer.

Then the cops got a break – of sorts. They found a reddish brown wig in the toilet system at Bambi's apartment block. A brown synthetic hair recovered from Christine Schultz's leg was very similar to the fibres from that wig. Then they discovered a hair recovered from the gag in Christine's mouth was not unlike Bambi's.

But it was still nothing concrete. The cops knew that Fred's gun had to hold the key. But it had already been tested by his partner the night of the murder.

On June 18 – a full three weeks after the murder – Fred, accompanied by Det James Gauger, picked up his off-duty revolver for test firing at the state crime lab.

Once again, Bambi looked on coolly as her husband and his colleague took away what was to become their most damning piece of evidence.

After stringent tests it was found to have been the gun that killed Christine.

On June 24, 1981, Lawrencia Bembenek was arrested and charged with the murder of Christine Schultz.

At a Milwaukee court in February, 1982, Bambi was sentenced to life for the killing. It took the jury three and a half days of deliberation and circuit judge Michael Skwierawski called it 'the most circumstantial case I have ever seen.'

A campaign was mounted to get the decision over-turned but all subsequent appeals failed.

Then, in August 1990, Bambi escaped from the Tay-cheedah Women's Correctional Institute in Wisconsin. She was helped by the handsome brother of another woman inmate. And the two proclaimed their love for one another before she made her daring escape.

Incredibly, the attractive ex-policewoman was still

protesting her innocence when she was arrested in Thunder Bay, Ontario, Canada, three months later. She had got a job as a waitress and was living under a false name with her lover.

Just before her escape, Bambi was asked by a journalist what she would do in her first hour of freedom. She replied: 'Have sex.'

The Greenhouse Gallows

Everything in Heathway was the same. The houses. The gardens. The street lights. Even the colour of the front doors.

It was one of those typical between the wars roads in a suburb that became a convenient overspill when London's population explosion really began to gain pace. The once neat rows of semi-detached three bedroomed houses had rapidly declined in appearance. Heathway also had other problems – like its location. Dagenham, Essex, is hardly the sort of place to inspire happiness. They say it peaked in the 1960s when the local Ford factory was churning out saloon cars at a rate of 100s per day. Then came the lay offs. Thousands upon thousands of Dagenham residents suddenly found themselves unemployable. It marked a turning point in the town's fortunes. Now, its biggest claim to fame is that it is the birth place of film star Dudley Moore.

But Dagenham has retained one thing – its reputation as a typical lower middle class London suburb. A place where armed robbers learn how to saw off shotguns. A place where Sharon and Tracey are two of the most popular names. A place where net curtains prevail in virtually every front room window. For behind that petty, finger wagging façade there are a thousand sins being committed.

Marriages come and go in Dagenham these days. The family unit is frequently split in two by divorce.

59

Neighbours are often locked in bitter feuds. But despite all this, the residents of Heathway like to keep up appearances. It might well be a scruffy little street littered with waste in every gutter. But it was still home to hundreds of ordinary, law abiding citizens.

Then there was Barbara Miller. She never really fitted in. Her parents George and Gladys sometimes wondered what they had done to deserve Barbara. She was just not the same as their five other children.

For a start Barbara did not even want to be a girl. Throughout her life she had longed to be one of the boys. She loved to play football, cricket and climb trees. She always kept her dark hair cut short. The longer she could fool the other kids then the longer she would be accepted. Of course the boys always found out eventually – and it broke Barbara's heart.

But that was nothing compared to what had happened to Barbara when she was just four years of age. It was an incident that scarred her for life and helped shape the following years of torment and waste.

She had always been a friendly little girl up until then. And it was no surprise that she befriended a local gardener in her favourite park. She would often accept gifts of sweets from the man. Barbara was just a small child. She did not know any better. But he did. He knew exactly what he was doing when he took little Barbara to an isolated piece of wasteland and ripped down her clothes.

When the terrified youngster was found wandering the streets distraught, a fundamental change had taken place in Barbara's character. The rot had already begun to set in.

The end result was a troubled life as a teenager and then an adult. Barbara, somehow, just didn't seem quite right. Dagenham was a brutal place for a misfit. And all the time in the back of her mind she kept remembering the horror of that attack on her innocent body.

Time and time again she was beaten up by other children. They used to tease her relentlessly about her hair. About her bucked teeth. About her being a girl. She wanted to be a boy to teach them all a lesson. She convinced herself that if she had been a boy then that monster would never have assaulted her. He was the root of all her evil.

Barbara bottled it all up inside herself. She never told her parents what was happening. She did not want to accept the fact – she was a girl. She just let the beatings continue. But they were inevitably affecting her life. They were etching hatred in her soul. Barbara had always hated certain people. Now she hated the world.

Perhaps George and Gladys Miller should have done something. They certainly saw the signs. But, like many parents, they chose not to say anything. To ignore it, hope it would go away. They were afraid it might push Barbara even further down the road to self-destruction. They were completely unable to put their feelings into words.

She came across to everyone as reckless and uncaring. The truth was that she was eaten up with guilt inside. She felt a failure. She had failed herself by allowing that animal to molest her.

Barbara felt that life had become one big bitch – and

she was going to take it for all it was worth. Sexually, physically, morally. By the time Barbara was in her mid-twenties she had long since lost her self esteem. She had waved goodbye to ambition. There were few jobs out there for a girl like her. She knew she had nothing to lose.

Barbara's only pleasure in life was the ultimate act – sex. She craved it day and night. Yet it was that very act at such a frighteningly young age that had damaged her temperament in the first place. What made it worse was that so few men were interested in her. With her closely cropped hair, jeans, T-shirt and hobnail boots she didn't turn many heads. As a teenager, she could only attract the boys by promising them literally anything if they would take her out. Her outlook on life was shaped for ever by that first horrendous experience and the subsequent adolescent sex behind bicycle sheds and in disused railway yards.

Sometimes the boys would line up and take it in turns. She knew it was wrong. But at least they were nice to her before they had their way. The trouble was they were invariably really horrible the moment they were done. But it hurt the most when none of them would even acknowledge her in the school playground the next day. It was as if she did not exist. She couldn't stand that. She would go to the toilets and cry. But she soon learnt to stifle the tears. The world hated her and she hated it back. What was the point of letting them get to her?

By the time Barbara left school at 15, she had become a regular visitor to the centre of London. She would skip off school and take the long tube ride up to Piccadilly Circus and wander the streets gazing at the bright lights of the big city. In her regulation uniform of short hair and jeans, she even managed to scare off the pimps that normally home in on young girls like Barbara. Those bucked teeth and cold, dark, staring eyes were like a sign around her neck that said: 'Keep Away. Danger.'

In any case, Barbara wasn't interested in selling her body. She had already been so badly abused by those animals that she did not care if she never slept with another man. If that was the way men behaved she wasn't interested.

But that closely cropped hairstyle and those boyish looks attracted another sort of predator. These intruders in her life did not abuse her and hurt her. They gently seduced her in a loving, caring, sensual manner. They touched her smoothly not roughly. They explored her and gave her pleasure. For the first time in her life Barbara began to discover what it was like to share her body rather than give it outright to some brute who only wanted to satisfy himself. By the time she was 18 years old, Barbara realised that the soft and caring caress of another woman was far more preferable to sex with a man.

Back in those days, she had always been the one seduced by older women. They would pick her up in clubs and bars. They would hardly make much conversation. They each knew what the other wanted. Barbara was a more than willing participant. She was experiencing something she had never come across in her entire life. A sharing experience. Giving and taking from the same person.

But as she got older those encounters got less and less frequent. It was as if the women were not interested in her because she was no longer a teenager. It seemed that the sort of women Barbara was encountering wanted 'fresh meat' not the old and soiled variety. And Barbara was starting to age rapidly. By the time she was 25 she looked almost 40. The toll of life was bearing down on her – and she knew it.

Barbara also realised she had to find a fresh approach if she was to continue finding satisfying female partners. She had let her hair grow during that period in her life. Perhaps that was the mistake? She now looked like an out and out woman for the first time in her life. Maybe that was what scared off her would be lovers?

Barbara decided to return to her old tried and trusted ways – she shaved her hair short, almost into a skinhead style. She wore baggy shirts and those short, masculine windcheater jackets together with loose fitting jeans that did not give away any tell-tale curves. The wardrobe was complete. Now she just had to find the girls.

Barbara was living back with her parents in Heathway by this time. The frustration of being sexually inactive was making her positively withdrawn. Now she had decided a plan of action. She felt good about it. She was going to find girls who were just like her when she was that teenager wandering the streets of London. They were the best. The ones whom she could teach. The ones whom she could love.

'Mum. I'd like you to meet Bobby. He's taking me to the pictures this afternoon.'

Jackie was just 16. But she had already had her fill of boys. They only wanted to use you and abuse you. They never tried to caress you and adore you. They only cared about one thing.

Now she was introducing 'Bobby' to her mother. Barbara Miller's guise as a boy was brilliantly convincing just so long as she did not open her mouth.

Barbara – or rather 'Bobby' – just nodded her head in acknowledgement toward Jackie's mother. But she couldn't help herself. She had to inspect the body of her new lover's parent. Her eyes travelled down over her breasts and then down to her crotch, a nestled swollen mound that clearly showed through her skin tight jeans.

Jackie's mother caught 'Bobby's' eyes as they stripped her and lusted after her. She felt a tingle of delight. She could read 'his' mind and she felt highly flattered. If only she had known that her daughter's 'boyfriend' was in fact a fully grown woman.

She watched lovingly as Jackie and 'Bobby' walked down the garden path hand in hand at lunchtime on that hot summer's day in 1987. They seemed to be laughing so happily together. They looked such a sweet sight together, she thought. If only . . .

Jackie and Barbara were laughing. In fact they were in hysterics.

'She fell for it. I can't believe it. She fell for it.' Barbara was holding tightly onto young Jackie's hand now. She was not going to let go . . . ever.

As they walked up the street towards Heathway, Barbara wanted to make sure that Jackie knew precisely what lay in store for her. Barbara began to tickle the palm of Jackie's hand with two of her fingers. Gently scratching and tickling. Then she pushed her forefinger deep into Jackie's clenched hand. In and out. In and out. In and out. Barbara just wanted to ensure that this pretty, silky skinned young girl got the message.

Jackie laughed as she felt Barbara's finger going in and out. She bent over and kissed 'him' there and then.

'I can't wait . . .'

The television was blaring. But no-one was watching it. A cat lay curled up by the gas fire desperate for some loving care and attention. The brass horses on the tiled fireplace looked as if they could do with a good polish. The swirly red patterned carpet had worn thin, tattered at the edges. Suddenly, a lamp stand crashed to the floor.

'Shit.'

Barbara Miller came up for air. She knew her parents would be furious if they found the lamp missing when they got home.

Lying underneath her on the sofa was Jackie. They were both naked.

'Come on Bobby. Come on.'

Barbara's momentary lapse was over. She looked down at the firm young body beneath her and knew she had to have more. She could not help herself.

Their lips locked tight on each other. Barbara opened her mouth as wide as she could and felt Jackie's slithery tongue exploring deep, probing into the walls of her mouth.

'Wider. Wider.'

Barbara commanded her young lover to open her mouth even more. She wanted to feel it's entirety with her tongue. She loved it when she ran it around

66

the inside of her gums and then across her smooth young teeth.

Sex with another female was so much better than with a man, thought Barbara. Little did she know that Jackie was thinking exactly the same thing at that precise moment. They had already climaxed twice earlier together. Now they were going for a third crescendo of lust. Nothing could stop them. Barbara started to run her tongue down Jackie's neck. Every few inches she would stop to kiss and suckle that soft, smooth skin. Then she carried on down towards the teenager's nipples. At first she gently slurped on them. Then she nipped them between her teeth and bit. Jackie let out a small squeal. It could have been a sign of pain or pleasure. Barbara did not care. She bit again. This time harder and longer. Then she lifted her head and watched the agony etched across her lover's face. It gave her even more satisfaction. Now it was Jackie's turn. She was firmly trapped under Barbara's body as they lay locked together on that sofa. However, that did not stop her sliding down past Barbara's breasts and lower. She stopped at her older lover's tummy button and began sucking air in and out of it. Barbara's felt the stabbing sensation from her stomach. It provoked a weird combination of feelings. She did not like it so she pushed her young lover's head further down.

It was not even 4pm by the time Barbara – or rather 'Bobby' – saw her lover home. Once again, they held hands tightly as they walked slowly and lovingly towards Karen's house.

And there was Jackie's mother waiting at the window

for a sighting of her darling daughter. But this time there was no smile on her face. No look of delight at the happy couple wandering along. Instead, there was a look of fury and hatred. Of disgust and shock.

For minutes earlier, Jackie's mother had met neighbour Vivienne Elliot in the street and she had told her about 'Bobby's' secret. Her daughter's 'boyfriend' was a woman. An evil woman who had just seduced her innocent child.

Barbara sensed something was wrong when the front door to Jackie's house flew open.

'You fucking dyke. Don't you ever go near my baby again. Do you hear me?'

Barbara heard her loud and clear. Her heart sank. She did not know what to say. She was going to try and bluff it out but that would hardly work. She knew that once she spoke, her secret would be out. She just had to know who? Who would be so evil as to tell on her? She had to know? She could think of only one person who would stoop so low. It had to be her.

Vivienne Elliot thought Barbara was seeing her first husband and she did not like it one bit. True. She had long since re-married. But that did not matter. He was still her property and she did not want some tomboy like Barbara sniffing around him.

The irony was that Barbara did befriend him. She had tried to 'connect' with him because she was desperate to change her ways. She wanted to give a man – any man – one last chance to prove that they were not really all that bad. They couldn't all be like that monster in the park all those years earlier or those uncaring boys who took it in turns to abuse her body. Surely they could not all be like that?

But now that potential boyfriend's ex-wife had given Barbara all the evidence she needed. Men were just not worth it.

'Don't you ever set foot in this house again. If I see you even talking to Jackie I'll fucking kill you.'

Barbara was shattered. She turned around and walked back towards the street. She was dead inside. At last, she had found some real love and lust. Now that was gone. Destroyed by an evil woman who did not care.

But Barbara did not feel any resentment towards Jackie's mother. She understood her reaction. It was perfectly reasonable. After all, she had just seduced her 16-year-old daughter.

No. It was Vivienne Elliot whom Barbara felt a rush of hatred for. That woman had just destroyed her love affair. The one thing that kept Barbara going now did not even exist. It was as if those hours of love making were just a dream. They had not actually happened. She had wrecked the one period in Barbara's life where there had been joy.

Barbara raged as she stormed her way back home to Heathway. The world around her was just a blur of distant images. The only world that now existed was inside her head. A throbbing repetitive pain. It seared through her mind, poisoning it with evil thoughts and deeds. She had to do something. She had to destroy her.

Barbara was sitting there in darkness when Karen Miller walked into the house less than half an hour later.

'What's up cuz? You look like death.'

69

Barbara said nothing at first. Her mind was still firmly entrenched in horrendous thoughts.

'Come on Babs. Tell us what's wrong?'

Karen was probably the only person in Barbara's life who even bothered to listen to her. She had been living at the Miller's house for most of her life because her own parents abandoned her. She called Barbara 'cuz' but in fact she was her niece. But they were more like sisters at times.

Barbara looked up at Karen and wondered. Perhaps this was a rare chance to pour out all her thoughts? It wasn't often that she had that opportunity. It was after all one of her biggest problems in life. She just never had anyone to tell.

'You don't really want to know Karen.'

'Of course I do cuz. Come on! Spill the beans.'

It was then that Barbara decided to change a habit of a lifetime.

'Hello. Vivienne. This is Karen Miller. You couldn't spare me a few minutes for a chat could you?'

Barbara and her niece had hatched a plot to destroy Vivienne. This was stage one.

'Great. I'll see you round here in a while then.'

Karen beamed as she replaced the telephone receiver. On the sofa – that same sofa where Barbara had made hot passionate love to her girlfriend just a few hours earlier – they discussed the next part of their scheme. By pure chance, Barbara's parents were away for the day. They had all the time in the world to get even with Vivienne.

* * *

70

Now Vivienne Elliot was not exactly a woman who oozed sex appeal. With her wire rimmed specs and penchant for seventies style clothes, she hardly made a sensual impression. But she must have had something going for her because she was never short of a man friend or two – or even three.

At 34 years of age and with four children by as many different men, Vivienne certainly knew how to live life to the full.

Her appetite seemed to know no bounds. She had become a virtual legend in Dagenham. She loved to go down to the local pubs and clubs dressed up to the nines in her favourite knee hugging, platform sole leather boots and a micro mini. Somehow, she would nearly always end up with a man in tow by the end of the evening.

Then there were the daytime sex sessions at the tiny two-bedroomed council house she lived in with the kids. She had a particular fondness for schoolboys. Neighbours would look on in wonderment as a stream of teenage lads poured into the house.

Vivienne used to adore the art of seduction. Drawing these nervous, shaking young boys into her bedroom by appearing in the front room dressed just in stocking and suspenders.

Then she would strip them and mother them before teaching them how to do it. Every now and again she would come across an experienced one – they were no good because she did not feel in full control. She hated it when they tried to dominate. Those boys would never be asked back.

She adored the really innocent ones. They were the lads she could mould and seduce. They would

71

do anything she commanded. Sometimes, that might include tying them to the bed – just to ensure they did not escape.

Once, Vivienne bound a boy head and foot and then gagged him before going to the shops. As she bought the week's shopping all she could think about was that young piece of meat back at the house.

By the time she got home she could not wait. She left the shopping in the car outside and burst into the bedroom. She did not care that he had virtually choked to death on that gag. She pulled it out of his mouth and sat on him without even bothering to untie the ropes.

But despite her flamboyance, Vivienne was still very possessive. She still liked to have her first husband under her control. She enjoyed allowing him to seduce her sometimes – even though they had long since divorced. And she was not at all happy that Barbara Miller had come on the scene. However, she would no longer be a threat because Vivienne had just made sure that everyone – including Jackie's mother – knew Barb was a lesbian. That would teach her.

As she walked around to see Karen Miller, she wondered if that was what the teenager wanted to talk to her about. Vivienne knew that Karen was probably Barbara's only friend in the world.

'Hello Vivienne. It's great to see you. Thanks for coming.'

Karen's greeting was as cordial as a meeting of two best friends when Vivienne Elliot arrived around at the Miller household. As she stepped into the front

Above: Lawrencia 'Bambi' Bembenek - sentenced to life for the murder of her husband's ex-wife.

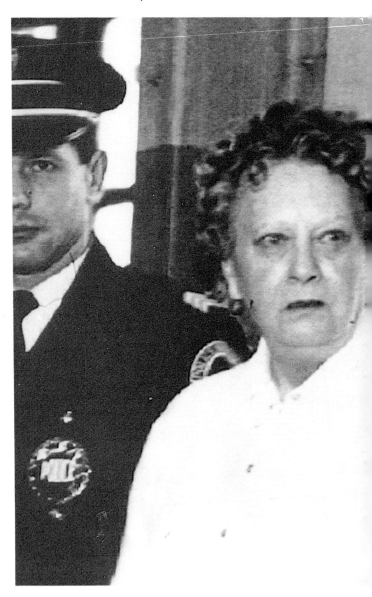

Below: She-Devil of Nancy : Simone Weber

Guilty: Waltraud Wagner

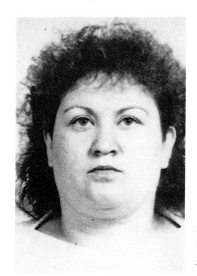

Guilty: Maria Gruber

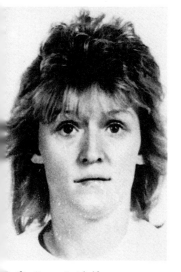

Guilty: Irene Leidolf

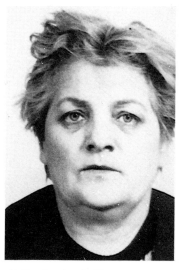

Guilty: Stephanie Mayen

Above: The four nurses of death.

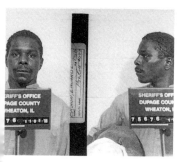

'Hitman' Eddie Brown

Far left: The house in Addison, Illinois, where Clarence Benkowski was shot dead.
Far left (below):Det. Sgt. Tom Gorniak of Addison Police, who immediately suspected Judy Benkowski
Below: Judy Benkowski marries lover Clarence Jeske inside Dwight Correction Institute, Illinois - August 1991

Judy Benkowski

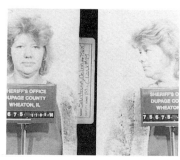

Debra Santana

Above: Paul Sainsbury - the jealous and bullying husband who paid th
ultimate price for abusing his wife Pamela for so many years.

bove: Pamela Sainsbury who was placed on two years probation after admitting the manslaughter of her husband.

Above: Sara Thornton - sentenced to life for the murder of her husband, Malcolm.

room there was no hint of the horrors that were to follow.

'Like a cuppa?'

The thought of a cup of tea was like music to Vivienne's ears. She'd had a tough day getting the kids off to school. Doing the week's shopping. Cleaning the house. Having sex with that cute 14-year-old boy who lived up the road.

'I'd love a cup,' said Vivienne. Little did she realise it would never actually materialise. Karen disappeared into the kitchen while Vivienne sat there on the sofa where a plan for her destruction had just been hatched.

Karen was excited. She had not hesitated when Barbara told her the plan. In fact, she thought Vivienne deserved everything she had coming to her. Karen had her suspicions that Vivienne had been sleeping with her last boyfriend. It was only logical for her and Barbara to decide to finish Vivienne off for good.

'She's here. Just stay in the garden. I'll get her out.'

Karen was in the kitchen whispering so Vivienne would not hear. Barbara just stood there. Her glazed eyes said it all. She was shaking with anticipation. The end of Vivienne's life was approaching.

'Come out in the garden with me. I've got something to show you.'

Vivienne never stood a chance as she stepped into that tiny garden in Heathway, Dagenham. Karen was the first one to get a direct hit. She turned and swung a clenched fist right at Vivienne's face. You could hear the crunch as her glasses twisted and fell to the ground.

Vivienne had not even seen Barbara standing behind her with a rolling pin when it crashed down on her head

73

a split second later. The onslaught had begun. But there was a lot more to follow.

Her body slumped to the stone pavement after Barbara's attack. The two women were surprised. They hadn't expected her to be knocked unconscious after just one hit with the rolling pin.

They stood there frozen for a moment. A look of disappointment came over Barbara's face. She had been looking forward to smashing her skull over and over again. She wanted to see the agony contorting Vivienne's face as she literally bashed it to bits.

Instead, her victim lay collapsed in a heap on the ground.

'Come on. Let's take her to the greenhouse.'

Barbara was now very much in command. This was her operation. She enjoyed the responsibility. It wasn't often she got to do something useful.

Karen and her aunt did not feel the slightest bit of remorse as they dragged Vivienne's semi-conscious body across the grassy garden. Suddenly, the dog next door barked. Karen and Barbara stopped in their tracks. Vivienne's limp body thumped to the ground. They waited there in complete silence fearing that the neighbour might appear in the garden next door. The fence between their homes was a mere four feet high. He might see them. That would be a disaster.

Barbara and Karen felt a bigger surge of fear run through their bodies at that moment than at any time during the evening. They felt no guilt about Vivienne. But they did not want to get caught.

Nothing stirred next door. Even the dog did not bark again. Their bloody escapade could continue undisturbed.

Barbara took the arms and pulled. Karen tried with difficulty to carry the legs but they kept dropping to the ground. As they neared the greenhouse, Barbara's strength gave way as well and they dropped Vivienne with an almighty crash.

They both looked down at her now. delighted in the knowledge that she would never again threaten their happiness. Ecstatic by the thought that she would soon be dead.

Just then Barbara looked down at Vivienne's bare thighs, exposed by that rough ride across the garden. For a second, she felt a twinge of lust building up inside herself. Maybe Vivienne could be used for one last moment of sexual satisfaction?

Barbara lent down and ran her hand up Vivienne's cold leg. She stopped at mid-thigh and squeezed it. It felt quite nice. She let her hand slide further up. Vivienne's semi-conscious eyes fluttered. Barbara's touch had stirred her. But she did not try to stop it. Perhaps she thought she might be spared if she let Barbara carry on?

'Bloody hell Babs. Are you a sex maniac or what? Let's just get her into the greenhouse for fuck's sake.'

Karen was the more sensible of the two. In any case she wasn't interested in other women. Never had been. Never would. Yet she wasn't shocked by Barbara's brief attempt at a sexual assault. She knew all about Barbara's perversions. She also knew what had caused them.

But she was well aware that this was no time for Barbara's uncontrollable lust to take over. They had things to do.

Inside the greenhouse, they heaved Vivienne's body onto a wooden chair. Then, once more, Barbara took control. First she tied Vivienne's wrists together. Pulling the knot so tight she could feel her victim wince with pain. Then she got down on her knees and began wrapping the rope around Vivienne's ankles. Barbara pulled rigidly on the rope to make sure it really was secure. But she was aware that Vivienne's thighs were parting right in front of her very face. Despite tightly tying those ankles together, Vivienne was showing Barbara what was there. Her thighs were opening wider and wider now. Inviting Barbara to push her hand up there and probe.

Barbara's breathing speeded up. She was having difficulty containing herself. She wanted to let her hand wander up there and explore the soft mound. Vivienne's thighs were on a level with her face as Barbara crouched there on both knees. She looked into Vivienne's eyes. They weren't staring at her as you might expect. There was no fear in them. They were saying: 'Do it. Go on do it!'

Vivienne was fighting for her life the only way she knew how – by acquiescing. This might be her only chance for survival. She would do anything to save herself. She would have opened those thighs to the entire world if it gave her another few minutes longer to fight back.

Barbara was trying to contain herself now. She was trying to resist the urge for self gratification because that is what it would have been. She was just a few inches away from the most sexual part of any woman's body. It was there waiting for her to finger and more. Much more.

'Fucking hell Babs. Let's just finish her off. Forget all that you dirty cow.'

Vivienne had just lost her final battle to live.

Barbara and Karen began to construct a make-shift gallows before Vivienne's very eyes. She was forced to watch as they made the method of her murder absolutely clear to her.

Barbara knotted the rope into a large noose and then threaded it through a long metal ladder that was fastened across the roof of the greenhouse. Vivienne struggled desperately. She rocked back and forth on the chair in a bid to fall over. She succeeded just as Barbara stood on another chair to test the effectiveness of their do-it-yourself gallows.

She jumped down and bundled Vivienne back upright. Karen then held her down by the shoulders to make sure it did not happen again. Barbara put her face right up against Vivienne's and told her: 'Your day has come.'

Then she forced the noose roughly over her head, scraping Vivienne's ears in the process. This was worse than any public execution. There were no last rites. No final request. Not even a hood to hide the fear.

Vivienne felt the prickly rope digging into her neck gently at first. Then Barbara yanked hard and the older woman started to choke.

Karen watched it all in a trance. It just did not seem real. It wasn't really happening. Finally, they were getting the revenge they so dearly wanted. But it did not feel the way she expected it to. Karen felt numbed – not excited anymore. Barbara pulled with all her might and tightened the knot holding the noose in place. Then she pulled the chair from right under her love rival and watched as Vivienne's head twisted upwards. The rest of her body crumpled onto the greenhouse floor but her head and neck remained locked to one side. For a few seconds, spasms of life twitched through Vivienne's body. Her head raged from side to side furiously. But that only made her death come quicker. It tightened the grip on her throat.

Barbara and Karen watched quietly as Vivienne gave up her fight to live. Barbara actually felt elated by the murder. It was as satisfying as the sex she had contemplated with that corpse just a few minutes earlier.

But now there was the matter of the body. It had to be removed.

No-one gave Barbara and Karen so much as a second glance as they pushed the wheelbarrow along the crowded streets. They had only covered 200 yards from their house so far, but it felt more like 200 miles to the aunt and her niece.

None of the boys they passed coming home from school that evening could have guessed that underneath a potato sack in the barrow was the randy housewife who had seduced so many of their pals. Vivienne would not be inviting any more of them around again.

As Barbara and Karen reached the corner of Heathway, they turned the barrow slightly to the right to avoid an old lady and the unmentionable almost happened. Vivienne nearly ended up on the pavement. It was a close thing. They felt the corpse shift position as they turned the corner and suddenly the barrow began to wobble. They envisaged scenes of utter horror as the body fell onto the street.

But it never happened. Barbara managed to regain control over the barrow and avoid it turning over. Then Karen noticed Vivienne's hand dragging alongside the barrow. She turned to see if anyone had noticed. There was not a sign of recognition from anyone. They were all in too much of a hurry to get home from school and work to notice two women pushing a corpse through a suburban street.

Karen carefully and discreetly pushed the hand back under the potato sack and they continued thier journey. She had not questioned the sense in Barbara's plan to dump the body. It was the right thing to do. What she did not realise was where Barbara was intending to leave it.

'You must be fucking mad Babs.'

Karen Miller was astounded. She could not believe that Barbara would be this stupid. Of all the places in all the towns in all the world, this was the one venue that would bring the police running to their front door within hours if not minutes.

For Barbara had decided to dump the strangled body of Vivienne Elliot in the woman's very own front garden. 'Just fucking do it!'

This was an order not a request from Barbara to her niece. Karen obeyed. Together the two women heaved Vivienne's stiffening body along towards the side entrance of the house. One of them struggled to open the side gate, while the other kept the body slumped upright. With one last shove they threw it onto the ground between the two detached houses. It was still late afternoon. There were lots of people everywhere, but no-one saw Barbara and Karen, Vivienne's body or even the wheelbarrow they hurriedly raced back home with.

*   *   *

George and Gladys Miller were in fine spirits when they arrived back at their home in Heathway just half an hour later. They had been visiting another daughter in Norwich and it had turned into a happy family reunion. And, since Barbara had not been invited, it was a peaceful occasion not marred by the usual squabbles that always seemed to follow their wayward daughter wherever she went.

But on their return home even George had to admit he was pleasantly surprised by Barbara that afternoon. She was giving the house a well deserved spring clean.

There was, of course, an ulterior motive. Their little home had seen quite a lot of life, sex and death that day. First there was the love making with Jackie then there was the plotting with niece Karen to kill Vivienne – and that was followed by the murder itself. Barbara would have to do a hell of a lot of scrubbing to clean out that house!

George and Gladys were blissfully unaware of all the horrors that had occurred just a few hours earlier. They were so relieved to see Barbara doing something to help around the house. Usually, she did absolutely nothing.

'Hi mum. Hi dad.'

She seemed like a different person. So cheery. So full of life. So vibrant. This was not the Barbara they knew. But her elderly parents never stopped to ask why she was so happy. They only thought about it later.

Outside the gates of the local primary school at about

this time, a little girl was looking distraught. All her friends had been collected but still there was no sign of her mummy.

Veronica may have been just five years of age but she was the spitting image of her mother Vivienne Elliot. It was eerie really – they could have been twins if the 27 year gap had not existed. The little girl even had the same sort of specs as her mum.

'Where do you think your mummy has got to?'

The teacher was very concerned. Vivienne was always very good about being there to pick up her daughter. Some parents were downright uncaring, but not Vivienne. She may have had a racy repu-tation around town but her parenthood was never in question.

They waited another fifteen minutes but still there was no sign of Vivienne. The teacher had no option but to ring Veronica's granny. Something could have happened to her for all they knew.

Iris Ives was puzzled. It just wasn't like her daughter to be unreliable when it came to collecting Veronica. As she picked up the youngster, she felt an odd feeling of impending doom coming upon her. Something was wrong. Something was badly wrong.

There was no answer at the door to Vivienne's house. Iris was confused. She had to be home. Where else could she be. She had to be home.

She tried again but still there was no reply.

'I'll go round the back granny.'

Iris thought nothing of letting little Veronica dash around to the side gate to the semi-detached house.

Her eyes followed her little grand-daughter's route and then stopped dead.

There on the ground were a pair of legs sticking through the side gate.

'Mummy. Mummy. Mummy.'

Iris knew it was her the moment Veronica began screaming. She dragged her hysterical granddaughter away from the corpse. It was way too late to save her.

Twenty minutes later police acting on a tip off from Vivienne's relatives knocked on the door of the Miller house and arrested Barbara for murder. Her niece Karen was charged with being an accessory.

Barbara told police: 'She was stirring it between me and my boyfriend. She deserved to die.'

The reality was a far more complex tragedy of life and death.

In July, 1988, at the Old Bailey, Barbara Miller, aged 30, was jailed for life after pleading guilty to manslaughter on the grounds of diminished responsibility.

Karen Miller, aged 19, admitted conspiracy to commit common assault and assisting to remove the body. She was given three years probation.

After the case, Barbara's father George said: 'My heart bleeds for both of them. They have had such a raw deal in life. I just hope to goodness they can get the help they need in the future.'

Death on a Waterbed

The shrill of a bell ringing loudly in the distance meant only one thing to Judy Benkowski. Her husband was demanding something.

Clarence Benkowski was overweight and overbearing. All his life he had been number one in that miserable household. And, even now, after retiring from his job as a welder, he expected to be waited upon hand and foot.

When his sick and aged mother decided to move in, it got even worse for Judy. Now there were two of them bullying and cursing her. Making her wait on them like a serf.

Often they would sit in the armchairs in the sitting room of Number 508 South Yale Avenue for hours on end without budging. That was when that little bell rang the most. An endless stream of demands came from her husband and mother-in-law.

RING – 'Get me a coffee,' said one.

RING – 'Get me a beer,' said the other.

RING – 'This coffee's cold, get me another.'

RING – 'This beer's bloody *warm!* Ever heard of a freezer?'

And so it went on. And on and on. Judy did not have time for a job in the outside world. Her full time occupation was looking after two bloated leeches and two ever demanding sons.

Sometimes it would all get too much. She would cry

herself to sleep at night. But that was only after Clarence had drunkenly tried to have sex with her. The act itself was totally one sided. He would make her fondle him and then – the moment he was ready – she would just lie there and listen to him grunting. It was always over in minutes if not seconds. But there was so much pain involved. Not love. Just pure and simple pain. The sort of pain that inevitably occurs when an overweight old man forces himself on a slightly built, five foot tall woman more than twenty years younger. They might have been husband and wife in law. But they were total strangers in the bedroom.

One day, Clarence had decided he wanted to spice up *his* sex life so he bought a waterbed. But, typically, it was the cheapest one he could find. The result was that Judy just lay there as usual every time he wanted sex – but now she had that awful, overwhelming sensation of rocking up and down as if on a boat bobbing across the ocean. But it did help in one respect: Judy used to feel so sea sick within seconds of Clarence starting, she would insist they stopped having sex before she puked all over him.

But Clarence's attitude towards sex was much the same as his outlook on life: the man ruled the roost. It was her own stupid fault if she didn't like it. She'd said the words: honour *and* obey . . .

For nearly twenty years, Judy had put up with the insults, the drudgery, the physical pain. What else could she do? She had no career. No existence outside those four walls. She had been trapped for so long she had forgotten what it was like to be free in the fresh air outside.

*   *   *

'You can't let him treat you like this. You've got to do something.'

Debra Santana was incensed. She had heard one story too many from Judy Benkowski. How could a husband treat his wife so badly? More to the point, how could someone put up with it? *She* certainly wouldn't.

'But,' Judy explained in her quiet, reserved way: 'What can I do. I have nowhere to go. No means of support.'

Debra was determined to help her best friend and neighbour. She was a striking blonde, now in her thirties, who had clung fervently to the fun-loving attitude towards life that she'd had as a teenager. She had suffered too. Her marriage had been terrible. But no soldiering on for her. She took the easy, and the sensible, way out – divorce. Now she was enjoying everything that Judy had long since given up hope of ever seeing. That consisted of a black, athletic lover who gave her the ultimate satisfaction and a life with few pressures.

Judy was very jealous of Debra's lifestyle. She so wanted to feel warmth, passion and true love again from a man. She knew Debra was right when she told her to end it. But how? What then?

Clarence would not even discuss divorce. His strict Catholic background meant it was out of the question. He would not even let her get on with her own life. She would have been perfectly happy if they had agreed to lead separate existences. She could have gone out with other men and he could have done as he pleased. But Clarence believed he owned Judy. She was his woman. If he demanded sex he should get it. If he wanted to insult her he could. If he wanted her to be his slave . . .

Naturally, this was an appalling prospect to Debra. She may have been thirteen years younger than her friend, but she reckoned women should always have fun whatever their age. And Judy was finding herself increasingly influenced by her younger, more outrageous pal. The more they talked about Debra's adventures, the more Judy began to wonder what life would be like without Clarence.

'So tell me brains, what do I do?' pleaded Judy, sarcastic and sad at the same time. 'In fact, what would *you* do? I'm trapped. There's no way out.'

The desperation in her voice sparked Debra's imagination. She had an idea. An extraordinary notion. But it would solve all Judy's problems if they planned it carefully. Oh, it would work alright.

'This is Eddie,' said Debra. 'Not only is he great in bed but he's also really used to this sort of situation.'

Eddie Brown had bestowed upon Debra all the sexual satisfaction she had ever craved. Even fully clothed, his physique was unquestionably beautiful. Biceps filling his sleeves taut, a chest straining his shirt buttons to breaking point. Judy felt a little surge of excitement as she shook his hand. She wondered just what sort of outrageous sex her friend enjoyed with this athletic, dusky lover.

But there was one thing about Eddie that did surprise Judy. He was just five foot three inches tall. In fact, Debra towered over him by a good four inches. But she winked at Judy:

'He more than makes up for it in other ways you know. Anyway enough of that, we've got serious business to discuss.'

Debra had not finally introduced her fantasy-come-true lover to Judy to discuss his sexual prowess. Eddie was going to do a job for Judy.

A job that required a certain amount of scheduling.

'Do you really think you can kill him without being caught?'

Judy finally broke the ice with Eddie. The introductions were over. The pleasantries had all been used up. Now she had to confront him with the facts.

And the facts were that he had agreed to murder her husband in exchange for a fee of $5,000. Now they had to sort out the finer details. Where should it be done? What weapon should he use? How could they make sure the police did not suspect anything? What if he survived?

For a few moments, Judy wondered if she had gone completely crazy. How could she even contemplate murdering another human being, let alone her husband?

'Maybe we should think about all this,' she said.

There was a brief silence from her two accomplices.

'What?' said Debra. 'After all he's put you through. You're trying to tell me you've changed your mind. We agreed on this Judy. Come on. Let's do it!'

Then Eddie chipped in, 'Yeah. It'll be easy. We can make it look like a random shooting. No trouble.'

The pressure was mounting on Judy. She wasn't a strong willed woman at the best of times. She sensed there was no choice in the matter. He had to die. It was her only escape route from a miserable life. The one way to break the deadlock which trapped her in misery. It might have seemed drastic but then what more did that animal deserve? He had treated her like dirt for too long. Now it was her turn. Revenge would seem sweet.

Before the dreams of a new life, however, there was the small matter of how and where to do it. It was mid-October, 1988, and Halloween was fast approaching. It's a celebration of death and ghouls. Why not do it for real? Judy had a great scheme. Or so she told her two partners in crime.

'Eddie, I'll get you a really scary costume. You're so short you'll look just like a kid out trick or treating. Then you knock on the door, Clarence answers and you blast him away with a gun. A trick on him, a treat for me.'

Debra and Eddie looked stunned. This was a preposterous plan. But they could also tell that Judy was deadly serious. She seemed really attracted to the ghoulish aspects of it. She even laughed excitedly as she described the plot.

'That'll teach him. He never likes to give anything to anyone who comes knocking at the door.'

Judy was really getting into the mood to murder. Her initial nervous approach had suddenly been replaced by a zeal that astounded her two friends. It was as if she had now fully accepted the whole plan as a *fait accompli*. The risk involved was being outweighed by the fast approaching scenario – the glory of life without Clarence. Judy was feeling happy inside herself for the first time in years.

'But hang on there Judy. Don't you think that might seem a bit suspicious,' said Eddie.

Judy was in no mood for doubters. Her voice rose: 'How? You tell me. *How?*'

Eager to make his point, Eddie replied calmly, 'Trick or treaters don't tend to gun down their customers. The cops would know it was a contract hit straight off. They'd be down on you immediately.'

Eddie was trying desperately to defuse the situation. Sure, he had agreed to murder this woman's husband. The guy sounded like he deserved it. But the scheme Judy had just described was insane. It was like something out of the mafia. Hardly the sort of low key killing Eddie had in mind. But Judy was having none of it. She reckoned it was the perfect plan.

'The cops will think some crazy trick or treater is out there blasting innocent people to death. They'll never think it was a contract killing.'

Debra and Eddie glanced at each other and shrugged their shoulders. 'You're the boss lady,' said Eddie. Jobless and just out of jail, he needed the money so he wasn't about to lose a contract as valuable as this.

Halloween is a major event in every town in America. Every October, across the country, trick or treat shops open in vacant stores for a few weeks and enjoy hectic business. There's a dollar or two to be made out of tradition. Hundreds of thousands of costumes are sold. Entire schools convert their halls and recreation areas into vast gothic dungeons filled with grisly spectacles like fake bodies in cardboard coffins, headless corpses and other reminders of the pagan rituals that originated the whole event. The schools and youth clubs charge a nominal fee for local people to be scared out of their wits in their home-made dungeon and some well-needed funds are raised for a worthy cause.

Just as popular is the trick or treating. This involves children dressed in witches costumes knocking on the doors of houses in their street and shouting 'trick or treat' when someone comes to the door. Inevitably a liberal helping of sweets are offered to the children and everyone goes home happy.

In the Chicago suburb of Addison, they celebrated Halloween just as fervently as the rest of the country. And South Yale Avenue – where the Benkowskis lived – was as traditional as it was typical. Row upon row of three-bedroomed detached bungalows built to maximize the use of space available. This was middle-class suburbia at its most classic.

Down the road at Debra Santana's house, Eddie Brown was for the first time in this entire episode, beginning to wonder what he had got himself into.

As Judy and Debra adjusted the ghoulish face mask they had bought for him at the local Halloween store, he felt more like a kid going out for some fun than a professional killer sent on a deadly mission to seek and destroy someone's elderly husband. To make matters worse, the latex mask was agonising. They had insisted on getting one that covered his entire face so that no-one could see what colour he was. But Eddie was starting to think he might never make it to number 508 alive at this rate. It seemed so difficult to breathe. He was already gasping for air and he hadn't even left the house yet!

'This is crazy. I can't even see properly out of the eye slits.'

Eddie's voice was so badly muffled by the mask, the two women did not hear him at first.

So he yelled: 'I SAID, THIS IS CRAZY.'

If Eddie had to shout this loudly to be heard, then he would probably alert the entire street when he went knocking on Clarence's door.

Yet more evidence that this entire plan was doomed.

Eddie then struggled to the window to see how active Halloween was looking out there. His face dropped. Well, it would have if he had not had that latex mask on.

There were literally hundreds of kids wandering the nearby streets doing the rounds. It seemed as if the entire population of under fifteens in Addison had decided to hit South Yale that night.

Eddie ripped off the mask in a fit of fury and stood there in his white skeleton costume. He started to jump up and down on the spot.

'I am not doing this. I can't shoot the bastard in front of hundreds of kids. I'd never get away with it.'

Eddie had come to his senses just in time. This plan had always had the ring of insanity about it – he had to kill it there and then before it was too late.

Judy was furious. She had woken up that morning with a new outlook on life. She imagined herself just 24 hours away from never having to see that ugly hulk of a husband again. Now Eddie had destroyed her morbid fantasy.

'You made a deal, Eddie,' she said, her voice low and threatening.

'Don't get me wrong Judy. I'll kill him. But not tonight. It would be crazy and we'd all end up in jail.'

Eddie was right. Or so Judy reluctantly agreed when

she had stopped and thought about that mad scenario. She might have wasted $25 on a ghoul's outfit, but it was nothing compared with the $5,000 she was still determined to pay to waste her husband.

'OK. What do we do then? You've got to go through with it.'

Eddie was as good as his word. 'Right. Let's start all over again.'

Judy agreed to postpone the 'hit' for a week. Eddie had convinced her they would get away with it only if they planned it meticulously. And he had a scheme that he was sure would work.

RING: 'Where's my breakfast? Come on I'm hungry.'

RING. RING. RING.

Clarence Benkowski was about to be served breakfast in precisely the same way he had been for the previous twenty years. In the kitchen, Judy Benkowski muttered quietly under her breath: 'Don't worry. You'll get it in good time.' She snarled a smile to herself. The big moment was fast approaching. Stage One of the 'hit' was about to occur.

But then, if Clarence had not been so incredibly lazy, he might have got up from the breakfast table and lumbered into the kitchen and seen Judy pouring the contents of 20 sachets of sleeping pills into his coffee.

Clarence, however, was not about to change a habit of a lifetime.

RING: 'Come on. I'm starving.'

Clarence was helping Judy to sentence him to death.

By ringing that bloody bell yet again he was signalling the beginning of the end of his life. He was guaranteeing that Judy would feel no guilt as she emptied every morsel from those packets and then swilled it around in his coffee. The more he rang that bell, the more she felt good about it. She knew she would never have to hear that noise again. It was a wonderful feeling – just to contemplate the end of such an awful era in her life.

Just keep ringing Clarence. Just keep ringing my fat shit of a husband . . .

Everything was ready now. Judy had a new spring in her step, a new bounce in her walk. But in her haste to impose a slow, lingering death sentence, she rather clumsily tipped the empty pill packets into the rubbish bin. She did not think about it at the time.

'Here you are darling.'

She hadn't called him that for years. 'Darling' was a term of endearment. How could she even contemplate feeling warmth towards the man she was about to have murdered. But she did for a split second. Judy was only human after all. It was merely a momentary lapse though. Judy felt a tingle of excitement as she put down the tray on the breakfast table. She sat, as she had always done, at the table and sipped gently at her tea. She could not help it – her eyes kept straining upwards and across the table towards Clarence. He hadn't even got anywhere near that coffee yet.

But then Clarence had his priorities. He always liked to gulp down his fried eggs first and stuff some toast in that huge cavern of his. Judy knew his habits only too well. That cup of coffee would soon be lifted to his lips. Be patient. Relax. He's going to drink it. All in good time. All in good time.

The *Chicago-Sun Times* was spread across the table in front of him, as it always was each morning. Something caught his eye. He stopped eating and gasped at the sports results.

'What the fuck? How could they have lost?'

Never over breakfast, had he made conversation with Judy for those twenty long years. Clarence was not about to break the habit of a lifetime. But still that coffee remained untouched. Judy's initial burst of excitement was rapidly changing to desperation. Come on! Come on! Get on with it! She could no longer hold herself back.

'Darling.' (for some weird reason she used *THAT* word again). 'Darling, drink your coffee. It'll get cold if you don't.'

For a split second, Clarence looked at his wife quizically. She *never* spoke at breakfast. Why the hell was she nagging him to drink his coffee? Never before in more than twenty years. Why now?

But, as with most things in Clarence's life, he gave it only a brief thought. Anything more would have required analysis. Something best left to the football commentators he watched every evening on the television.

Judy was annoyed with her weakness in the face of such adversity. What on earth was she doing trying to make him drink the coffee? It was a sure way to guarantee he'd get suspicious.

She held back for a moment. Looking down at her own cup of tea. Not daring to raise her head in case he caught her eye. Then he might see the signs of guilt. He might even spot the murderous intentions that filled her mind as they sat there at that last fateful breakfast.

Maybe she had blown it? Perhaps he'd sussed her out? She shut her eyes for a split second in the hope all that doubt and anguish would go away.

Then, finally, he did it. The harsh slurping noise came like music to her ears. She opened her eyes once more. Now he was gulping it down at a furious rate. Desperately trying to wash away all the grease down his gullet. It was his favourite way of eating. It was a disgusting spectacle for everyone else. She had never dared suggest he improve his manners. Now he was paying the ultimate price. And for once it was a beautiful sight.

First one whole cup then another followed in quick succession. Judy could feel the rush of relief running through her veins. She sighed quietly to herself. It was, she reflected, the greatest achievement of her life.

'I don't feel so good. I think I'll lie down for a while.'

The magic words Judy had been waiting to hear. Eddie had said precisely how many she should feed him. Not too many, he insisted. They should knock him into a deep slumber rather than complete unconsciousness. That way no-one would be able to tell he had been drugged.

Now Clarence was struggling towards the bedroom. They had taken effect. So far everything was going according to plan.

He only just managed to get to that wretched waterbed before collapsing in a heap. Judy crept into the room after him – just to make sure he was out.

*   *   *

95

'He's asleep. You better tell Eddie and get over here.'

Judy slammed down the phone and awaited her two accomplices. Debra was the first to arrive at the house. She hugged Judy warmly. She wanted to make sure her good friend knew that she supported her completely and utterly.

The two women sat side by side on the sofa in the front room and counted the minutes until Eddie arrived. They soon heard the back door opening and their hired killer walked in. With an eerie silence, Judy handed Eddie her husband's World War Two Luger pistol and motioned him towards the master bedroom.

Debra meanwhile put on a pair of stereo headphones and started listening to heavy rock music. It was a bizarre reaction. Maybe she was trying to blot out the noise of the gunfire that was about to occur?

The two women were once more sat down on that same sofa. Eddie had said he would use a pillow to muffle the sound but that did not stop Judy from hearing the exact moment when her husband died. It was a strange kind of thudding noise. Nothing like what she had expected. But she knew that was it. A feeling on immense relief flowed over her. It was over. At last it was over.

But there was more work to be done. Judy and her two friends had to make it look like a burglary that had gone wrong. The two women and Brown began tearing the house apart to make it look convincing.

They pulled drawers of clothes out and spread them all over the bed where Clarence lay under the covers. The waterbed was still intact. No leaks despite the hail of bullets. Judy wasn't sure if that was a good thing or not. She really did hate that waterbed. But then it would have caused such a mess if it had leaked everywhere.

Then she gasped with anguish. Eddie was about to start making the place look turned over downstairs. But there were limits to such authenticity.

'No. Not the china.' Judy was insistent. There was no way Eddie was going to be allowed to destroy her vast collection of china memorabilia. She had lovingly collected it over years and years. It was the one possession in that house she cared about.

'But this is supposed to look like a burglary.'

Eddie was only trying to be a thorough professional. He wanted to make sure the cops were convinced. Judy would have none of it.

'Just leave it. We can still make it look good without ruining everything.'

Eddie just shrugged his shoulders. She was paying him so it was up to her. But he certainly would have done things a lot differently.

Within a few more minutes, it was time for Eddie to make his escape out of the back door. But first he wanted his down payment for the job. Judy handed over $1,000 and let him take two rings from a jewellery drawer. The rest would be delivered to him within a week.

Seconds later Eddie was gone. Now the whole scenario was starting to dawn on Judy. Debra could clearly see the relief on her friend's face. The two women embraced once more. They had done it. They had got rid of the animal. There was a big wide world out there waiting to be conquered. They were on their way. They had right, if not exactly God, on their side.

But before they could leave the ransacked house,

they needed to make sure the coast was clear. First Judy checked down the street. It was mid-morning: husbands at work, mothers out shopping. Deadly quiet. Debra glanced out of the back door just in case. But there was no-one around. Time to celebrate.

The Italian restaurant was so crowded that Judy and Debra were hardly noticeable. The only unusual thing about them was that they ordered a bottle of expensive white wine. Few people drink alcohol at lunchtime in middle America. But then Judy and Debra had good reason to propose a toast.

'To us. Long may we live.'

It sounded innocuous enough. But if only some of the other customers realised what those two women were so happy about. If only they had known that just one hour earlier they had witnessed a brutal killing that they had organised. Perhaps it was entirely apt they should celebrate in an Italian restaurant. After all, they were acting like a pair of Mafia contract killers.

But it wasn't just a new life that Judy was looking forward to. She reckoned Clarence's life insurance would be worth at least $100,000 and then there was the $150,000 mortgage paid house.

Mrs Benkowski was going to be a very merry widow indeed.

'He's been murdered! He's been murdered!'

Judy's screeching tones sounded truly horrific to Addison cop Det Sgt Tom Gorniak. He had been patched through to the Benkowski home after the nearby police station had received an emergency call from Debra and Judy, who had discovered Clarence shot dead on their return from a shopping trip.

In a three-way conference call between his patrol car, the police station switchboard and Judy, he was trying to ascertain what had happened as he rushed around to South Yale Avenue.

Gorniak had no doubts this was a genuine call. He was facing his first murder enquiry in a month. Within minutes he was on the scene.

An ambulance had already arrived when he got to the tidy, white painted house. Gorniak immediately consoled the two women and got a uniformed officer to escort them from the house.

Then he began a detailed inspection of the property. Gorniak knew he could not disturb anything until the crime scene technicians arrived, but he was well aware that this was the best time to look around. To get a feel for what must have happened.

Within minutes, he found himself puzzled by certain aspects of the crime. At first, he couldn't quite work it out. Then he realised what was bothering him.

The victim's body was laid slumped in bed as if he had been taking an afternoon nap. How could he have slept through the noise of an intruder who then leant over him and fired three bullets into his head at close range?

Gorniak knew that few burglars would do that. In fact, few would even carry a gun and even if they had, they would have been reluctant to use it. A good burglar gets the hell out of a house if he is disturbed. All he wants is the goods as fast as possible. If someone stumbles upon him, his first response is to run – not shoot. No, thought Gorniak, this victim was asleep when he was shot. He did not even have time to turn around and see who his killer was.

Then the policeman noticed the clothes thrown from the drawers over the body. That meant the killer had ransacked the room *after* the shooting. It just did not make sense. This guy would have got out of there as fast as possible following the shooting.

Gorniak had been a policeman for ten years. He knew how dangerous it was to draw any conclusions at such an early stage in a murder enquiry. But this most definitely looked like a contract killing.

'Did your husband have any enemies Mrs Benkowski?'

Det Sgt Gorniak was trying to be as gentle as possible. After all, this was the widow he was talking to and she seemed really cut up badly.

No. He had no enemies.

Gorniak had a hunch, nothing more than that. But it was enough to make him persuade Judy to stay on at the police station for a little longer that evening. He explained to her that he knew how awful she must be feeling but it really would be in everyone's interests if she stayed behind. Judy agreed. She did not want to appear to be hindering the police enquiries in any way.

Gorniak and his colleague Det Mike Tierney began to gently probe the widow for clues. They were convinced there was still a lot more to tell about this case. Judy, meanwhile, was getting edgy. She knew she had to tell them something. Maybe a half truth would solve her problems. Then they would leave her alone and go after the murderer?

'I did see someone outside the house this morning,' she recalled.

Gorniak and Tierney raised their eyebrows. Why didn't she mention this before? How could she have forgotten to tell us this earlier?

Judy then described how she had returned from her shopping trip with her friend and they had seen this rather short, stocky black man.

'Now I come to think of it, he did seem to be running away from our house,' said Judy.

The two officers were astonished. They started to pull in the reins a little bit. They sensed that Judy knew more than she was letting on.

The next step was to haul Debra Santana in for questioning. As the detectives waited with Judy for her friend to arrive, they tried an old and trusted technique.

'It would help us if you could tell us everything you know,' said Gorniak.

Judy waited for a moment. It was just like a weight-lifter pausing before lifting a barbell over his head. She had a lot of weight on her mind and those officers knew it.

'I know the black man who was running from my house. His name is Eddie Brown. He is Debra's boyfriend.'

Tom Gorniak and Mike Tierney were about to hear a full confession to murder.

In September, 1989, Judy Benkowski cried when she was sentenced to 100 years in prison for hiring a hitman to murder her husband.

Du Page County prosecutor Michael Fleming had argued that Benkowski should receive the death penalty.

But Judge Brian Telander ruled that there were mitigating factors that 'precluded the imposition of the death penalty.'

These included no prior criminal record, numerous health problems and several character witnesses who testified on her behalf.

Fleming described the sentence – which means Benkowski will not be eligible for parole until she is 97 – as 'fair and appropriate. She claimed she wanted a divorce and he wouldn't go along, but she never even talked to a lawyer about it.'

On August 31, 1991, Benkowski married sweetheart Clarence Jeske at the Dwight Correctional Institute, in Illinois. The couple had first met before her husband was murdered but they both insist their relationship did not begin until after the killing.

By a strange twist of fate, Jeske now lives in that same 'house of death' in South Yale Avenue. He has been made legal guardian of Judy's two children by her marriage to Benkowski.

The Children slept on

She had an affinity for light. Her skin was luminous. Her dark hair glistened. But it was the brown of her eyes, like jewels on velvet under a storekeeper's spotlight, that were the source.

He looked into them, felt their warmth, oblivious of the darkness to come. For somewhere, within her stunning beauty there lay a twisted mind. A mind warped by time. A mind that wanted him all to herself. A determination to get what she wanted – no matter what the cost. How dearly the innocent would have to pay.

But for the moment, Lydia Galladan just wanted her lover Augusto Pineda. She wished to obey his every command. She wanted him to be her master.

Augusto could barely endure her presence without feeling an overwhelming lust for her. Every time he looked at her, he thought of the passion, the unashamed love making that knew no bounds. He knew she would do anything for him. It was an extraordinary sensation – knowing that your lover would obey any request, however bizarre. Lydia just could not refuse. She was obsessed and infatuated with Augusto. He had made her perform sex acts she never even realised existed. But she did not hesitate in her quest to satisfy. If he wanted it that way – then she would do it. Her own enjoyment was a bonus. If she felt a surge of excitement as well then that was good. But if it did not happen, then there was always another time, another place. It was far more important to Lydia to serve her master. To please him in every way possible.

On this day in September, 1982, the red flames of passion were burning brightly between the two lovers. It was mid-afternoon but it could have been midnight for all they cared. The curtains in the bedroom of the tiny apartment were closed. But the lights were on. Augusto always insisted on the lights being on. He wanted Lydia to see as well as hear everything – in graphic detail.

They had arranged the rendezvous the previous day in a coded phone call.

'Ok Mr Galladan I will see you at three.' Augusto wanted to make sure that no-one knew where he was really going.

Now they were about to seal their lust for one another yet again. Within seconds of getting through the front door of that modest flat in Philbeach Gardens, Earls Court, South West London, they started.

Lydia took his coat slowly off his shoulders, stroked his neck, kissed him full on the lips. There was no point in making conversation. They both knew what was about to occur. But Augusto liked Lydia to do everything for him. It was sort of traditional in his family. The female would honour and obey the man's every command. In any case he was sure she enjoyed it.

No sooner had she removed his coat than she knelt down in front of him and ran her hands from the top of his thighs down to his knees. She kept both hands spread so that her nails dug slightly into his skin through the flannel material of his trousers. She knew he could feel a tingle. A subtle sensation as her thumbs rode up and down the inside of his thighs. So near and yet so far.

Augusto's only response was to spread his hands through her thick, luscious hair. Then he held her scalp firmly, almost roughly for a moment. Excitement surged through his body. His breathing quickened. He looked down at the crown of her head, covered in those dark, silky locks.

Lydia was still on her knees. Probing him with thin fingers. She wanted it to last for ever between them. She would not rush the act – unless he wanted to. Augusto appreciated her gentle touch but he wanted more. She was there to serve his every whim.

He stopped stroking her hair, and grabbed at it more roughly, pushing her face towards his groin. She did not mind the slight pain of her hair being pulled. She knew he was giving her a sign. He wanted her to take him all the way. She could feel the stiffness through his trousers. Throbbing against her cheek. Then she kissed him through the material. Not enough, he wanted more; he wanted it *now*. He dug nails into scalp and pushed. It was time for her to unzip his trousers.

The first time Augusto climaxed, she felt nothing. No satisfaction for her. He made no attempt, no move to turn her on. But that did not matter to Lydia. She had already consumed the evidence of his own lust. Now, they were about to start again.

But first, she had to remove her clothes. She knew he would never even attempt that for her. In any case, he liked to watch her undress herself. He enjoyed the pleasure of watching her perform a private striptease just for him. And Lydia was happy to oblige. She was

105

obsessed. She would do anything for him. Absolutely anything.

He could not resist the way she looked at him while she slowly and sensuously removed each garment. Her hair fell forward, across slightly slanted eyes. Each time it covered her face she would flick it back and look straight at him. Then her tongue would push out from between her full, pouting lips and lick the rim of her mouth from one side to the other. Just thinking about where that tongue had been made Augusto rise to the occasion.

The strip was important to Lydia as well. For it marked the only moment in their sessions when she was in charge. When she could provoke him. When she could control *his* lust. In many ways, it was the most exciting moment for Lydia. Maybe if she had stopped to think about that then she would have realised just how dangerous her obsession was becoming. But Lydia did not consider it. She was built to serve her master.

Now she was down to her red bra, red stockings and matching suspender belt. Slowly and provocatively she unhooked the bra, leaving it hanging there for a few moments. There was just a hint of her shapely breasts below the line of the bra. She ran her hands up her stomach – slowly, ever so slowly. She watched him watching her. Once again running her own tongue around the rim of that pouting mouth. Then she pushed her hands up and under the bra and squeezed her breasts hard. She knew he liked it when she did that. But Lydia had not yet finished. She held both bosoms out towards her lover. Pointing them, invitingly, towards him. Then she knelt on the double bed and began rubbing her nipples between thumb and forefinger. She squeezed

106

them fairly tightly to ensure they would grow quickly. Within seconds they had become bullets, hard and aimed at him. Lydia closed her eyes for a moment and soaked up the pleasure she was giving herself. If only he would do it to her sometimes.

She removed the bra completely, crammed her breasts together and lent over her lover's face, smothering him with the fullness of her body.

Lydia was in ecstacy. At last she was close to climaxing. They had been making hot passionate love for almost three hours but this was the nearest she had been to satisfaction all afternoon. Augusto might have come three or four times already but then he was not really interested in Lydia's contentment.

Suddenly, as if by some cruel stroke of fate, the door bell sounded. Lydia was so close and yet so far. She tried to keep going. She wanted Augusto to carry on. Don't stop now! Not now! But the bell rang continuously. Mocking her. As though there were some deliberate plan to stop Lydia climaxing, to ruin her one and only moment of sheer enjoyment. She tried to keep going but the noise was too much.

'Please Lydia. It might be an emergency. You must answer it.'

Augusto was quite relieved the door bell had interrupted them. He had long since passed the point of satisfaction. It was actually becoming a bit tedious now – in any case it was almost time to go to work. The bar where he served was expecting him there at 7pm

The bell was still shrilling away as Lydia pulled herself off her lover and wrapped a pink silk dressing gown around her naked, burning body. Who could it be? What was happening? Lydia unhooked the latch and opened the door. She could not believe her eyes.

Bella Pineda was shaking with rage as she rang the bell, her mind scarred by the knowledge that her own husband – the father of their two children – was in this flat having sex with that *slut*. It was just a few days before she was due to give birth to a beautiful bouncing baby boy.

She knew what was happening because she had followed him all the way there. She did not want to believe it. In fact, she had sat there – hot and uncomfortable – in her car outside the flat for nearly three hours before she decided to confront them. She knew they could not have spent all that time just talking. They had to have been *screwing* together. There was no doubt in her mind. She just felt so betrayed.

'You bitch. Where's my husband?'

Lydia was stunned. For a split second she stood there in silence. She just did not know what to say. She tried to wrap the silky nightgown more tightly around her lithe body. It was a strange reaction to the situation – almost as if she did not want her lover's wife to see what he had just devoured.

'I don't know what you're talking about.' Not exactly convincing and she knew it.

At that moment, Augusto appeared. When Bella saw him, it really was the ultimate insult. Her husband and his lover standing there almost naked while she stood by, heavily pregnant with their baby.

'If you are not home in one hour then I never want to see you again.'

Despite the situation, Bella was still prepared to forgive. She did not mean what she was saying. She just wanted to make sure he returned. She loved her husband very very much. She would do anything to make him happy. She was there to serve and obey. But then both women were orginally from the Phillippines. Their subservience had been ingrained deep within them from an early age. They had a lot more in common than they ever realised. Both existed solely for his pleasure.

Now, even as she stared at the evidence of her husband's adultery before her very eyes, Bella thought only of how to hold on to him. She wanted to make sure that other woman could never have him all to herself. She wobbled away from the apartment feeling a strange mixture of sadness and satisfaction. She had suspected Augusto was seeing another woman. Now it was out in the open and he would have to end it. Bella would never return to that flat ever again.

'Look Lydia. I don't think I can see you for a bit. It's better if we don't meet.'

Augusto was struggling to get his clothes on as he tried to explain to his mistress why they would not be making love ever again. But Lydia was not going to accept it all that easily.

'But I want you. I want to be your wife.'

Augusto cringed. What had he done? This was supposed to be an innocent love affair. But then how can any illicit sex be innocent?

He said little but decided a lot. He was not going to see Lydia again. It was not worth it. In any case, all this talk of marriage was really worrying him. He wanted sex not love. Couldn't she understand that?

'I'll be in touch.'

Augusto did not sound very sincere as he left the flat that day. But what else could he say? For her part, Lydia read the blank spaces between the words alright. But she could not contain her love for Augusto. She had to have him. He was her salvation. Without him, she was just a lonely nurse living in a big, unfriendly city.

'Hello Augusto. I must talk to you . . .' CLICK.

Lydia's heart sank when the phone line went dead. She dialled the number once again.

'You must talk to me. Come round tonight . . .' CLICK. It happened yet again.

Lydia could feel the resentment building up inside her. She had to see him. He could not just discard her like this. 'He said he loved me . . . He said he loved me . . . He said he loved me.'

The words kept ringing through her head. She picked up the phone once more and dialled the number.

'I love you Augusto. How can you do this to me?' CLICK.

The phone went dead for the last time. Lydia thought about Augusto. Lucky Augusto. Happy Augusto. The man who had everything. A wife, two children and a pretty lover. He had it all and she had nothing. She could not stand to even contemplate him getting into bed later that night with his wife after having kissed his two children goodnight. He had what she wanted.

She could not bear it. It had to change. She would not give him up that easily. There had to be a way to win him back.

Lydia sat and thought for hours and hours. Every time a plan came to her she dismissed it from her mind because it was too outrageous. But she could not get him out of her head. She thought back to all the passionate love making. The things he used to say to her.

It was then she decided. She had devised a scheme. She reckoned it could work if she planned it carefully. She was obsessed. She had to have him.

The underground train was virtually empty on that early morning of September 6, 1982. It was travelling out of the centre of London to the suburbs when millions of commuters were going the other way. In one carriage, there was a solitary figure staring demurely out into the blackness of the tube. She seemed to be in a trance. Even when the train stopped at a station her eyes did not waver, did not follow the people getting on and off. She was just looking into a huge nothing. A cavity of emptiness. She felt no emotion. Just steely determination. She often thought this way when she about to perform some unpleasant task during her work as a nurse. It helped to divorce herself from the reality. It made the most distressing moments much more tolerable. But this time, Lydia Galladan was about to perform a special duty – one just for her own, tiny, insignificant little self.

She got off at Balham Underground Station. The sun shone brilliantly, market stalls lined the nearby streets, crammed with bustling crowds. But she walked in a

111

vacuum. The grey, tatty cheap shop fronts might as well not have existed as far as Lydia was concerned.

She opened the A to Z street directory and marched up Tooting High Road. It wasn't far. In any case, she would have walked a 100 miles to find this particular house. It could have been a war zone anywhere in the world – it would have made no difference to Lydia. She was going to get to that house and perform her duty. Her only wish was to love and obey him and she was about to make the ultimate sacrifice. Soon she would have him all to herself. She neared the house in College Gardens, Tooting. But there were a lot of people in the street and she did not want them to notice her.

She waited at a corner discreetly. Watching and hoping. Then it happened. She saw Augusto leaving the house. Again, she held back just to make sure he had not forgotten anything. She knew he had an early shift at the bar that day. He would not be back for hours.

Lydia walked casually towards the small terraced, red brick house. She passed it without a glance. There were three builders opposite. She did not want them to notice her at the front door. She did not want them to see her break in. She returned to the street corner in frustration. It was no use while the builders were there. And she could not exactly hang around on the street corner much longer without attracting attention.

So what? she thought. I'll go through with it regardless. She walked back to the house and stopped at the front garden.

'Hello darling.'

The builder's wolf whistle was a form of flattery to Lydia. She returned the compliment with a soft smile.

But she knew it was no good. She had been seen. What could she do?

Then it came to her.

Lydia started to pick some of the beautiful array of late summer blooms in the front garden. She would make sure those builders thought she was tending to the garden. For twenty painstaking minutes, she pretended to clear the weeds and other bits and pieces from the flowerbeds. The builder's wolf whistles had long since subsided.

Inside the house, Bella Pineda was blissfully unaware that she had hired a new gardener. Across the street, the builders were getting thirsty. It was almost nine and they'd been on the job for more than two hours. Perhaps it was time for a good old fashioned British tea break.

As the four burly men walked off up the road to a nearby cafe, Lydia saw the opportunity to fulfil her duty to Augusto. She knew what she was doing was right, was just. She felt safe behind that knowledge. It gave her the resolve she needed.

It would not be difficult to get into the house. While she had been pretending to do the gardening, Lydia had spotted a ground floor window with an insecure catch. Ever so quietly she slipped the catch on the bay window and silently pushed it up just far enough to allow her the space to climb in. It was a typical front reception room of a modestly sized Victorian terraced house. Toys were spread across the floor. A TV set on a badly made shelving unit in the corner. Beige carpet – perfect to hide a multitude of sins. Two very plain sofas. No-one around. Lydia was pleased. This was perfect. The element of surprise was all important.

Slowly, deliberately, she crept through the room

towards the door at the far end. Then she heard a wingeing, whining sound. It seemed like a hell of a loud noise to Lydia in that silent and tense atmosphere. She stopped in her tracks. Sounded as if it was in that very room but there was no-one around. She continued walking but there it was again. This time it was slightly quieter but just as disturbing to the soul.

Lydia looked down at her feet. She had kicked a teddy bear with her foot. It had grunted the first time she connected with it. Then it had rolled over and grunted again. This was the nearest she had ever been to his children – the children she wished she could have by him. For the first time that day, Lydia felt a twinge of fear. Somehow that teddy bear's grunt had scared her. Maybe it was the first evidence of what was to come? Or perhaps it reminded her of the task she was about to face?

Lydia reached the door. She opened it ever so gently – just in case there was someone in the hallway. The door creaked painfully. She stopped for a second – afraid she would be heard. There was no-one around.

Then she heard it – the unmistakeable cry of a tiny baby coming from an upstairs room. She had heard the same sounds so many times before in the Cromwell Hospital where she worked. But this was different. This was *his* baby. The child he had by her – the woman who would not let go of Augusto.

'There. There. There Michael.'

Another unmistakeable voice. Her lover's wife. The woman who had wrecked Lydia's happiness. She was invigorated by that voice. It inspired her to continue. The time was approaching.

But first, a suitable weapon. Lydia went to kitchen.

114

It did not take long to find the drawer with the biggest knives in it. The sounds of the new born baby upstairs and his attentive mother carried on throughout. They gave Lydia strength. They motivated her. They also covered the racket she was making.

Now she was on the stairs. Clenched in her right hand was a huge 12 inch long carving knife. As she slowly climbed the steps, it glistened slightly in the mid-morning sun. Lydia stopped on the landing. The cries of the baby had subsided. The mother had obviously got him to sleep. She had better move fast before he awoke. She hoped her lover's other son Donkelly was resting. It would make it all the more easy. She had to get Bella, before she left the bedroom.

She leapt up the last few stairs. There was a spring in her step now. It would be so wonderful. Just him and me, just him and me, she thought.

She burst through the door in a frenzy. In front of her lay tiny ten-day-old Michael in a cot and his elder brother in another cot next to him. They were both asleep. Bella, however, was very much awake.

'Get out of here. Get out.'

Bella showed no fear. Just hatred. Pure and unadulterated hatred. She saw the knife clearly enough but she would never be afraid of Lydia. Her only emotions towards her were seething anger and resentment. This was the woman who tried to steal her husband. This was the illicit lover who tried so hard to ruin her life. And she had the audacity to threaten her with a knife she didn't have the guts to use?

The moment Lydia heard Bella speak it purely affirmed her determination to get him back from her. This was it. There was no going back.

Bella stepped towards her. She might as well have committed suicide there and then. The knife plunged into her left breast, tearing at the flesh, grating metal hard against bone.

The children slept on unaware of the life and death struggle between the two women in their father's life. Lydia twisted the handle of the knife to cause maximum damage. Her rival crumpled to the floor as she pulled the blade out.

But Lydia wasn't finished yet. For a moment, she stood above Bella's contorted body and stared down at her. It was a satisfying stare. A look of contentment. But there was more to come.

The children slept on.

Lydia leant down and held the knife in front of Bella's face. She wanted to see that defiance turn to fear. She longed to watch those eyes fill with the dread of impending death. And they were. The self-assurance was gone. Brave Bella was no more. Just a quivering wreck with a gaze locked on the knife. Too scared to blink. Too weak to move.

Calmly, sweetly, Lydia stabbed her in the throat. As the prick of the blade jutted into the windpipe she felt the handle quiver slightly, slicing through the gristle. Then she pushed doubly hard and the knife pitched in through the throat and came out at the back of the neck. It was a fast, furious movement. There was no resistance from the victim. She was already going to another, safer, world.

And still the children slept on.

And still Lydia was not finished.

She had to be sure. She had to know that he was now all hers. She craved for the security he could offer

116

her. She had to make sure. She stabbed at Bella's other breast. It felt like one of those sacks soldiers pierce with their bayonets. Lydia wanted to mutilate her, destroy the beauty of her rival. To make sure that if he ever saw her body then he would be so repulsed he would have to turn away. That was how she wanted Augusto to remember his wife. A mess of bloodied garbage . . .

She twisted and turned the handle each time just to ensure the maximum damage. Blood gushed out of Bella's breasts and throat in torrents. But no atrocity would deter Lydia. For her, it was quite beautiful. Natural justice.

And still the children slept on, unaware.

It was around the twentieth stab that Lydia stopped for a second to examine her handiwork. The body in front of her was clearly drained of life and much blood. But something inside drove her forward. She had to destroy the body in such a way he would never look at her again.

She lowered the dripping blade and pulled up her victim's skirt. Once again, she started to plunge the knife in. Twenty-one, twenty-two, twenty-three, twenty-four, twenty-five, twenty-six, twenty-seven. There was little or nothing recognisable left.

Then ten-day-old Michael stirred. At last one of the two other human beings in that room had been disturbed by the murder that had been committed just a couple of feet from them. He began to cry. It served one important purpose. It stopped Lydia from continuing her dance of death. The sound was unbearable. Shrill and piercing. Lydia looked down at the tiny infant. She could not stand the noise. It had made her regain her senses but she had wanted to remain in that insane

117

frenzy. She would have carried on butchering that body if he had not cried.

But now she had to do something about it. There was only one answer – little Michael needed a bottle. Lydia was a nurse after all. She knew how to cope in trying times.

Leaving the baby crying there in a room filled with bloody carnage, she calmly walked down the stairs to the kitchen. In the sink she soaped her bloodied hands and arms in much the same way she had done at the hospital a thousand times before. Some of it had turned into a maroon crust on her skin. She had to scrape hard to remove it. But the sight of blood had never bothered her.

Then, having scrubbed herself clean, she carefully simmered the infant's milk before filling a bottle. It was extraordinary – almost as if she were the mother of that child rather than the murderer of his mother.

After pouring the contents into the bottle, she even tested the milk on the outside of her hand – just in case it was too hot. No. It was perfect.

Who said she was not a caring person?

'There you go little chap.'

It was just like being at the hospital for Lydia as she leant into that cot and lifted her lover's infant out and put him on her lap. She had frequently bottle fed newly born children when their mothers wanted some rest. On this occasion the mother would be at rest for ever.

And baby Michael took to the bottle as if it was being given to him by his very own mother. She could feel and hear the sucking noise of the teat being strained by the hungry infant. It did not take long for him to settle once more. She placed him back in his cot gently and carefully. Making sure he was on his tummy not his back – she did not want him to choke after that feed.

On the floor beside the two cots lay the bloodied remains of their mother. Puddles of red had appeared around the corpse where the blood had gushed out so ferociously only a few minutes earlier. Lydia glanced at the body casually. She felt no emotion. Only satisfaction that at last he would be hers. *She* could not stand in their way anymore.

Even so, her duty was not quite yet complete.

Lydia walked over to the wardrobe and looked through the many brightly coloured dresses hanging in neat rows. Her eye was caught by one very pretty and expensive looking flowery cotton garment. She took it out and felt the material. It was thin, almost papery in texture. Perfect for what she required.

She crumpled the dress up and dropped it next to the partly clothed remains of Bella Pineda. She stopped and glanced at the two children sleeping so peacefully in their cots. They would never know, she thought to herself. They would never know.

Lydia lit the match and dropped it onto the dress. Instantly it caught fire. A look of total satisfaction came over her face. Now she had done her duty finally and completely. They would start a new life together. He would have no past to tempt him back. She had destroyed that for good. Or for worse . . .

* * *

The flames swept slowly through the room, as Lydia walked down the stairs and let herself out of the front

119

door. No-one in College Gardens that day even noticed her leaving. Not even the builders who had admired her so much just a few hours earlier.

Lydia quickened her pace to try and get away from that street before the alarm was raised. She need not have worried. The flames devoured those two little children and the corpse of their young mother before anyone even realised there was a fire.

Inside that dreadful room, the stench of death would remain forever. Those children never stood a chance. They choked in their sleep, still blissfully unaware of what had occurred. Perhaps that was some small blessing at least.

Lydia Galladan, aged 26, would never have been caught if police had not at first suspected Augusto Pineda of that horrendous mass murder.

After days of interrogation, he told police of her existence. She confessed within minutes of their arrival on her doorstep. It had taken the murder of Bella and her two small children to make Lydia realise she would never win back the love of Augusto.

At the Old Bailey on May 9, 1983, Lydia Galladan was found guilty of murdering Bella Pineda, aged 35. She was cleared of murdering the two children, but found guilty of their manslaughter.

Galladan told the court: 'I am sincerely sorry for the harm I have caused and I deeply regret the shame I have brought my parents and my vocation.'

Judge David Tudor Price told her: 'I believe the

deaths of the children will hang very heavily on your conscience.' But she showed little remorse for her murder of Bella Pineda.

Augusto Pineda, aged 35, returned to the Phillippines shortly after the case to try and start his life all over again. 'It started off as an innocent love affair. I know it was wrong but in my wildest dreams I never imagined it would end like this,' he said after the case.

Rivals in Love

Bill Buss felt as if all the worries of the world were heaped on his broad shoulders. He had worked incredibly hard over the last three years to build up the farm into a going concern.

But there were always problems. Then more problems. And then even more problems. As sole owner of a fifty acre farm, he had to absorb all those pressures single handedly. When should the harvest be picked? How many times a day did the cows need milking? How could he afford to maintain all that equipment? It was a never ending task. But farming was his life. He was good at it, and he had no other choice.

At 26 years of age, Bill Buss's one remaining ambition was to find the perfect girl and start the family he so desperately wanted . . . and needed. What was the point of flogging your guts out on the land if there was nothing to come home to? The eighteen hour days were gruelling but even they would all seem worthwhile if he could start a family. Then the never ending list of problems would not seem as bad. A homesteading woman, and perhaps even some healthy bouncing babies. That was the answer for Bill Buss.

Meanwhile, he had to continue grafting away. And the most important task on his agenda that evening was to organize the midnight milking of the cows.

For this was Eland, Wisconsin. And in middle America they take their farming very seriously. Bill was under great pressure to have a full quota of milk ready for the early morning pick-up by the dairy company tanker. It was a vital part of his income from the farm. It did not matter whether it was twelve midnight or twelve midday, the job had to be done and Bill was the only one there to do it. It was his responsibility to have that milk ready for a dawn pick up. It was also his income that would suffer if the dairy company did not get every drop he could supply.

But the worst part of it was the waiting. He could not milk the cows any earlier because they would not yield the maximum quantities. That meant Bill had to literally force himself to stay awake for the midnight session. Sometimes, he would be so tired after a full day's work that he would go to bed at around nine, set his alarm for 11.45 and try to get a few hours shut-eye before heading for the cow sheds.

But on this particular evening, he struggled to stay awake in front of the television. Flicking channels continually as a way to eliminate the boredom, he sat there with a glazed expression. Bill was not a great TV fan. He found it difficult to concentrate on the banal ingredients that make up much of American television. But it kept him awake and that was the most important thing.

As midnight approached, Bill made himself a hot coffee. It was mid-September in Eland and the nights already had a certain bite to them. The dew came early in those parts and that always brought a slight chill to the air. In any case, a hot drink might help snap Bill out of his sleepiness.

On the stroke of twelve, Bill wandered into the vast cow shed to connect the FILL IN to each of the dozens of cows that stood there, resigned to their regular fate. Bill never really gave it much thought – did these animals mind having their udders emptied in such a mechanical fashion? They certainly never seemed too upset but then no-one had really bothered to ask them their opinion. And they wouldn't have got much of an answer if they had.

Within thirty minutes, Bill's familiar task was complete. He unhooked the FILL IN and shuffled back to the farm house for that desperately needed four or five hours sleep. He had to be up by 5.30 at the latest. A farmer's work was never complete.

'Bill. Bill. Open up.'

Bill thought he heard something. But then again he might have been dreaming. He stirred ever so slightly but then fell back into that richly deserved slumber.

It seemed like he had only been asleep a few minutes anyway. He needed every second of sleep he could get.

But then why did a dream wake him up? Maybe there was someone outside? He grappled for his watch on the bedside table. It was 12.45. He had only got into bed ten minutes earlier.

But now everything was once again silent. It was that eerie silence that fills the air with its presence. Perhaps it was something particular to the open countryside. There were no roads nearby, no gentle buzz of a car engine or the siren of an emergency vehicle. Bill's farm might have been close to town, but there were wide open spaces for miles around.

Bill fell back to sleep. He had obviously been dreaming. What about he was not sure. But his exhaustion was such that it would take a hell of lot more to stop him sleeping.

'Bill. Bill. Open up. I must talk to you.'

Now the high-pitched voice was accompanied by a steady banging on the door. The way Bill heard it, it sounded almost muffled but then that often happens when you are asleep.

'Bill. I know you're in there.'

Bill had no choice. If he was going to get any sleep at all, he had to answer the door. He knew who it was and it annoyed him. He just wanted to stay snuggled up in bed. He certainly did not want to lose another few precious minutes answering the door to *her*.

He wrapped his dressing gown around his aching body and shuffled to the front door.

'Alright. Alright. I'm coming.'

Now, under normal circumstances, Bill might have rushed to the door to find out what all the comotion was about. Perhaps there had been an accident nearby? Or maybe some of the farm animals had escaped?

But he knew who it was at the door that night. And he was fed up to the back teeth with *her*. Why couldn't she just leave him in peace. It wouldn't be so bad if it were the middle of the afternoon but this was just *too* late.

Lori Esker had no such qualms. She wanted to see Bill and she did not care what time it was. Her love for him was so strong that she felt he should have been happy to see her at any time of the day or night.

Lori just could not get Bill out of her mind. She found herself eating, sleeping and fantasising about him every moment of her day at university in River Falls Wisconsin.

She could not hold herself back any longer. She had to see him. She thought nothing of getting in her car and driving the 125 miles from college to Bill's farm. It was a small sacrifice for love.

However, Bill was not inclined to feel the same way about Lori. She might well have been an attractive, curvaceous blonde 20-year-old. She might even have been the 1989 Dairy Queen in Marathon County. And she was certainly a girl whom many men would die for the chance to love.

But none of that meant anything to Bill. Sure, he had had a love affair with Lori after he and yet another dairy princess, Lisa Cihaski, had split up. In fact, Bill had found Lori extremely attractive at first, but he was a cautious sort of guy and she was, well, just a bit too much for him to handle. But he did not regret his passion for Lori. They had a great time together while it lasted. And Bill certainly had Lori to thank for something very dear to him – his on-off-on again romance with Lisa.

You see, all Lori's sexiness had taught Bill that Lisa was the right girl for him. Basically, he could now see what a fantastic girl Lisa was – compared with Lori. It was what you might call the classic rebound.

But Lori had not taken her rebuff that lightly. She interpreted all that passion with Bill as a sure sign that they were meant for each other. Sex meant love to Lori. She had given her all to Bill and then he had turned around and rejected her. In the tightly knit farming communities of rural Wisconsin that was easier said than done.

Now she had come around to Bill's home to lay claim to what she rightly saw as hers. He was not going to get off that lightly.

*   *   *

126

As Bill unbolted the front door, he knew exactly what to expect. After all, in the three weeks since he had ended his affair with Lori she had been virtually haunting him. This was obviously going to be the price he would have to pay if he was to revive his love for Lisa.

But Lori refused to even acknowledge the existence of Lisa. As far as she was concerned, Bill was her property. She had given herself to him in every sense of the word.

'Oh Bill. I'm sorry if I woke you.'

Lori was not sorry at all and Bill knew it. What he did not realise was the extent to which he was becoming the sole object of her fantasies.

Before leaving college that night for the long drive to Bill's home, Lori had found herself swamped with desire for Bill. She had been planning to leave directly from the campus classroom to drive to Eland but as she sat in the lecture hall her mind wandered to the last time she had made love to Bill. She remembered every detail of their passion.

When class ended, Lori decided she had to make a quick diversion to her digs at the other end of the campus. It would only hold her journey up by a few minutes, she thought. She could feel her breath getting uneven with the expectation that she would soon be with Bill once more.

As she burst into her college room, she was relieved to see that her room-mate was not around. Lori ripped open the wardrobe. She wanted to find something very special to wear for Bill.

For a few moments she panicked. Where was it? Maybe she had left it at home? She had to find it. She wanted to use it to convince Bill there was still a great physical need between them.

At last, she saw it hanging there. Just finding it had aroused her. She laid the silk all-in-one teddy on her bed and pulled out a small suit case to pack a few other overnight belongings. The teddy was really a skin-tight negligee – the same shape as a swimming costume but with an even more extreme, plunging neckline. Around where a woman's breasts would snugly fit were edged see through lace. Lori was about to put the teddy into the bag when she stopped momentarily. She sat on the edge of the bed and tried to picture the scene later that night. The scene she hoped would seal her love for Bill.

She recalled how shy Bill always was as she thought about those first few inevitably awkward moments whenever they began kissing. She always had to lead the way to the bedroom, undo his trousers, fondle him and then show him where she wanted to be stroked and caressed. He would always want to immediately push his hand between her legs. She had to teach him that there was more, much more, to a woman's desires. Bill would also often lose interest if Lori decided to dart into the bathroom to quickly change into something sexy for bed. By the time she reappeared, he would often have drifted off to sleep

That made Lori decide to take some defensive action. I'll put it on now, she thought to herself. So, she peeled off her tight fitting jeans and blouse and bra and slipped on that slinky, sexy feeling negligee. Lori could already begin to feel a certain warmth running through her body.

As she pulled it up over her milky white thighs, she momentarily closed her eyes and thought of what she hoped was to come later that evening. She was standing in the middle of the room pulling the straps of the teddy up and over her shoulders. It was a really snug fit. That smooth, silky material felt warm against her cold nipples. She could feel them going erect. She began to wonder if she could hold herself back for the next few hours.

For a few moments she stood there in the room and looked at herself in the full-length mirror. Her left hand moved up to touch the blue silk where her nipple was pressing against the material. She could feel a tingle running through her body down to between her thighs.

She sat down once more on the edge of the bed and let her right hand travel slowly down across her flat stomach to the tops of her legs. She was trying desperately to resist the urge to push her hand down between those thighs. Her legs opened just enough for a noticeable gap to appear. Her fingers were pressing and stroking the flesh just inside the tops of those thighs. She was only half an inch away from the mound she so desperately felt the urge to stimulate.

But she thought better of it. I have to save myself for Bill. It will be much better that way. It was a real dilemma for someone as sexually keyed up as Lori, but she wanted it to be something really special with Bill that night. She was going to do everything imaginable to win him back. If she satisfied herself now, it might detract from that eventual, all-consuming pleasure.

Hurriedly, Lori pulled on a figure hugging skirt and a loosely fitting blouse. Making sure it was open just enough to reveal a glimpse of the see-through edging of the teddy where it covered her breasts.

Then, as a final touch, she put on her highest,

newest, white stiletto heels. The seduction uniform was complete. Back at Bill's farmhouse at that ungodly hour, Lori neither knew nor cared about her ex-lover's exhaustion from a hard day at work. She just wanted a guarantee that her unashamed seduction techniques would lead to the long term love she was convinced she deserved.

Bill blinked through his sleepy, weary eyes at Lori. He really did not need this one bit.

'Lori. Why don't you just go home. It's so late and I'm exhausted. Please. Let's talk in the morning.'

But Lori could not hear him. She was stripping his body with her eyes. His hair may have been ruffled. He might have looked unkempt with a full day's stubble, but she loved him all the more for it. She pushed into the house and shut the door firmly behind her.

'I want you Bill. I cannot stand it. I have to have you. I want every part of you. Make love to me now. Here. You have to.'

Now, many men might have succumbed there and then to Lori's advances. But not Bill. He had made a commitment to Lisa. He had even asked her to marry him. In any case, he was dog tired from his exhausting work schedule. Sex was the last thing on his mind at that moment.

'Go home Lori. Just leave me alone. It's over.'

Once again, Lori was not listening. She wanted what she wanted and nothing was going to get in her way. Bill did not know what to do. Lori had called around late at night before but she had always eventually accepted his pleas and turned around and left him. But this time she seemed like a woman possessed. Her eyes were fiery and alive with lust and obsession all rolled into one.

Usually, by this stage in the proceedings, Lori would have just walked out of the house. But on this occasion she was not budging. For a moment, Bill looked at her. He had to confess she looked gorgeous. The high white stilettos had somehow given her more poise. By adding those extra inches to her height, it seemed to accentuate her curves. The tightness of that pencil thin skirt where it covered her shapely bottom and the fullness of her firm breasts pressing hard against the silk blouse. He remembered how much Lori loved the feel of silk against her bare skin . . .

Bill snapped out of his trance. He had to get Lori out of that house somehow. He was not prepared to risk losing Lisa for a silly one-night stand. In any case, that was not the way Bill Buss ran his life. He was an honest, decent citizen who just wanted to lead a perfectly normal, trouble-free existence.

'I am going to bed Lori. You can stand here all night if you like. But I've got to get up early.'

Bill stomped away towards his bedroom. He was seriously pissed off but he could not think of any other way of handling the situation other than physically throwing her out of the house. And Bill was far too much of a gentleman to even consider that option.

Maybe now I can get some peace, he thought as he slipped back into bed. He was convinced she would let herself out of the front door and leave him in peace for a few hours. Lori Esker had no such intention.

She had been thinking through every moment of her great seduction scene for the three hours it took to get to Bill's home. She had her own masterplan and she was about to put it into action.

She had to act swiftly. She did not want Bill to fall

asleep – then he would be useless. She craved for physical satisfaction as well as that long term aim to be his wife and mother to his children.

Standing there in the hallway of the tidy bachelor house there was only one thing for it. A plan that no man would be able to resist.

Lori hastily unbuttoned her blouse. It dropped to the floor. Then she wriggled out of her tight fitting skirt. Anticipation flooded through her veins. It was just like earlier when she changed her outfit at college, but this time the object of her desires was just a few feet away.

Wearing just that dark blue silk teddy and those high white heels, Lori walked slowly through the darkness towards the bedroom she had once got to know as well as her own.

She opened the door silently. It was as if she was a burglar desperate not to be heard. The truth was that she was an intruder and she had plans to steal Bill's body. Not surprisingly, Bill was already drifting off to sleep and did not hear a sound as his seductress crept into the bedroom.

Lori stopped momentarily and looked at Bill's broad, naked shoulders as he lay curled up like a young child in the double bed. She had to have him. Still ever so quietly, she lifted the sheet that covered him from the waist downwards and knelt over his body.

Both his legs were caught between her thighs now. She had him trapped. She could even feel the points of her stilettos sticking into her own buttocks. It was a pleasant, if slightly painful, sensation.

Bill was shocked. He knew exactly what was happening. But he could not actually comprehend what

Lori was trying to do. She must be crazy, he thought to himself. He lay there too stunned to move. In any case, she had him firmly trapped between her thighs. There was no escape. But then how many men would want to get away from this?

'I am going to have you Bill. Nothing will stop me.' Lori's hand darted down between Bill's legs and grabbed at his penis. She started to stroke him. It was virtually impossible – even for Bill – not to start getting an erection.

'I cannot stop wanting you Bill. You have to satisfy me.'

Bill was wriggling now. Trying to loosen her vice like grip on him. While one of her hands continued caressing him, she began to stroke her own nipple through the midnight blue silk teddy.

Lori was telling Bill in her own inimitable way that if he did not return her passion she would still satisfy herself. And there was another, almost as strange, aspect to this as well. For she started to talk in fantasies – to tell him about her innermost thoughts.

'I love watching you on the tractor. It makes me excited to watch you with that thing between your legs.'

Bill was astounded. He had never heard a woman talk like this. Lori wasn't shocked though. This time she was the one driving that tractor, in a sense. And the sexual excitement was going through her body like a rush of adrenalin.

She closed her eyes and remembered how months earlier she had watched Bill on his tractor. She recalled how she would focus in on his buttocks as they jigged up and down slightly in motion with the movement of the vehicle.

She watched transfixed for ages. She kept speculating that maybe he had an erection as he drove the tractor. But then Bill was not really the type of guy you asked those sort of questions. Instead, Lori kept it stored in her memory bank for those lonely moments when she was lying on her own in her little single bed at college.

There was something about the tractor and the way Bill would sit astride it. She kept imagining she was that seat. She would fantasise that he was sitting on her, dominating their lovemaking. The reality of the situation was that she was always the one on top.

And, as she sat firmly on his naked body that night, she was reminded yet again of those sexual preferences. Bill, meanwhile, was dumbstruck. He did not know how to handle the situation.

A beautiful blonde, dressed in a silk, partly see-through teddy complete with white stilettos was trying to force him to have sex against his will – and better judgement. And Lori's enthusiasm knew no bounds. She was gently rubbing her body against his chest in a desperate attempt to get him aroused. Her left hand was still stroking his groin. Squeezing and then pulling at it. Never letting up. She would not let go. She wanted him to keep a full erection.

Then Bill snapped. He could not stand it a moment longer.

'Get out. Just get out and leave me alone. I don't love you. I love Lisa.'

Lori ignored Bill for a few moments still. She continued her desperate efforts to arouse him.

'Get off me. Just get off me.'

Bill's final outburst actually worked. Lori stopped in mid-stream. She clambered awkwardly off her former lover and walked out of the bedroom without saying another word.

Minutes later, he felt a great surge of relief when the front door slammed shut.

Bill hoped he had finally got Lori permanently out of his life.

'I'll pay cash. It's just that my grandma needs me to help her move house.'

Lori sounded desperate to the rent-a-car woman at Wolf's Auto Centre, in River Falls. She was really one year too young to qualify for a hire car but Kassandra Hotchkiss felt sorry for this well-mannered, attractive young girl. After all, she was going to help her granny.

'Just this time, we'll make an exception. But you make sure you don't get in any trouble.'

It was typical of Lori really. She had that sweetness and charm that almost always got her precisely what she wanted. She used to love twisting her mom and pa around her little finger. At the family's 450-acre farm in Hatley, Wisconsin, it was no surprise she ended up being crowned Marathon County Dairy Queen in 1989. She wanted that title badly, so she went out there and got it. Butter wouldn't melt in Lori Esker's mouth, they all used to say. And all the boys at Wittenberg-Birnamwood High School used to worship the very ground she walked on.

Back at the car rental office, Lori was delighted and relieved that she had managed to hire a vehicle. She had got a very important errand to run that evening. It was something that she was sure would change the whole course of her life. Lori wanted to be certain the lady in the rent-a-car office knew precisely why she was hiring a car. It was all part of one of those masterplans that Lori was so fond of having.

She also wanted a car that would definitely get her the 125 miles from college back to Birnamwood, where she aimed to make a very important rendezvous. The journey between River Falls and Lori's home area was mainly one long quiet interstate freeway much like many of the motorway routes that dominate the United States.

There was never much traffic on the road and that meant it was not the sort of place a young single girl should drive alone in a less than reliable car. Hence her decision to hire a vehicle.

The drive was fairly monotonous. The car had a radio but no cassette deck. Lori had to make do with some less than endearing radio stations blaring out rather dated 70s hits like the Eagles and Steve Miller. Next time, she thought to herself, I must make sure I ask for a car with a cassette machine.

But the easy drive did give her an opportunity to think about Bill. Even the way he had rejected her seduction attempt did not put her off. She convinced herself he was just a shy kind of guy and, in any case, it was Lisa's influence that was making him less responsive towards her. But Lori was going to do something about that.

Then Lori began thinking about the good times – the moments she was determined to re-live when he became her husband. Her mind began to drift once more towards her own private fantasy – his tractor driving.

Now she was nearing the moment when she could really influence their future together. That determination was in itself a pleasant sensation for Lori. She liked to be in control. She did not like losing at anything. She nearly lost Bill. Now she was going to win him back – whatever it took.

Lori's rented Dodge saloon car hardly stuck out amongst the other vehicles parked outside the Rib Mountain Howard Johnson Motel in Birnamwood. This was the sort of place where travelling salesmen make overnight stops during their high mileage trips from town to town in middle America. And the majority of them drove cars very similar to Lori's Dodge.

Lisa Cihaski had just finished her late shift at the motel and was walking towards her own car parked just near the Dodge.

'Hey Lori what you doing here? I thought you were at college?'

Lisa was surprised and edgy. There was only one possible reason for Lori to be there.

'I must talk to you Lisa. Now.'

Lori's voice was cold and unemotional. She was virtually barking an order at Lisa.

The two girls got into Lisa's car. There was no-one else anywhere in the car park that night. No witnesses to the horrors that were about to occur.

'You've got to stop seeing him,' said Lori. 'He's mine you know.'

Lisa was astounded. She had always known about the existance of Lori. After all, her love affair with Bill the first time around had long fizzled out when he met and fell for Lori. There was no suggestion of Bill two-timing one girl for the other. But Lisa was also painfully aware that Lori had been very upset when Bill had broken off that romance to go back to his former love.

There had been incidents in the previous few weeks. Like the time Lori had called her a 'bitch' and a 'slut' when their paths had crossed in a local bar. It was humiliating in public but Lisa did not really think twice about it. She put it down to a bit of old fashioned jealousy. She could not believe that Lori would take things any further.

Bill had not dared tell her about the midnight visits. The silky teddies. The high heels. The demands for sex. He probably knew she would find it difficult to believe that nothing had happened on those fateful nights.

Now Lisa was facing Lori alone. It could end in trouble but nothing she couldn't handle. Or so she must have thought at the time.

Lori had one great advantage over Lisa: she had been planning this moment for quite a while. She knew exactly how she was going to handle the situation. She wanted Bill back. She believed he was rightfully hers.

'You know, I may be pregnant by Bill don't you?'

Lori's outburst was deliberately timed for maximum damage. She had caught her rival off guard. Lisa was stunned. She did not believe Lori. She knew how obsessed she was. She was not going to give up her husband-to-be that easily.

It was a shock for Lori. She had calculated that Lisa would be knocked sideways by this revelation. She had convinced herself that it would destroy any love Lisa might have for Bill. But she could not have been further from the truth.

'I don't believe you. You're lying because you want him back.'

This was not all going according to Lori's carefully staged plan by any means. Lisa was showing the one characteristic that Lori did not know how to handle – unswerving loyalty.

Lisa believed in Bill. She had also known him for much longer than Lori. She knew he would have told her first. He was an honourable, simple kind of guy. He just did not deceive girls. That's why she wanted to marry him so badly. In Lisa's mind, that was precisely the reason why she would end up being Mrs Bill Buss not her.

'I tell you it's true,' said Lori.

It was a last desperate bid and it was falling on deaf ears. Lisa knew it wasn't true. Lori's plan had backfired. Now she had to think fast. She had no intention of just letting Lisa walk off with her man. She had thought she could warn her off with the pregnancy story. It was not enough.

'Get out of my car,' said Lisa. 'I never want to see you again as long as I live.'

She never would.

Lori looked around her inside that car. She wanted to do something to Lisa. She wanted to punish her for stealing her man. She wanted to leave Lisa with something she would never ever forget.

In the back seat of the car, Lori saw a blue belt. If she could somehow get to that belt then she could teach Lisa a real lesson.

Lisa, meanwhile, was getting impatient. She wanted Lori out of her car . . . and out of her life.

Something snapped at that moment. Lori leant over and grabbed at the belt.

Lisa could not fully comprehend what was happening. She looked quizically at Lori at first. Unsure what the other girl was doing by taking that belt from the back seat. Within seconds, Lori had wrapped that it around Lisa's neck. *Now* she had the upper hand. Now she could make her rival squirm, apologize for muscling in on her man.

The shock and surprise of what was occurring combined with the sheer brute strength of the heavier-set Lori was too much for Lisa to contend with. With a soft cry of terror, she tried desperately to pull the belt away from her neck. But she could not even get her fingers around it. The inside of that car felt icy cool as the belt dug deeply into her windpipe. She tried to grab at it but she could not summon the energy. Already, all that life was being drained away from her lithe young body. Her heart felt swollen by the sheer terror of what was happening. It was pumping furiously. She could feel it hitting her chest each time.

All she could see out of the corner of her eyes was the belt. It seemed to have a mind of its own. She could feel the heavy breath of her assailant but she could not see any part of her face. Then nothing but bars of light and darkness. Stars floating in front. The soft felt of the interior lining of the roof of her car went out of focus, merged with the light, closed in around her.

Pathetic whimpers squeaked out from between her lips. Little gasps that would have been screams but for the tightness of the belt. She tried one last desperate claw at her assailant. In the process she managed to draw blood from her own neck where her finger nail had pierced her skin as she tried to shake free.

Her head felt like it was coming away from the rest of her body. Her arms went limp.

'Bitch. Fucking Bitch.'

The venomous words spat from behind her echoed large and loud in Lisa's head. They were the last thing she ever heard.

Lori quickly realised Lisa was either dead or unconscious. She snapped out of her murderous trance and found herself facing the slumped body of her rival in love. But she had no time to consider the enormity of what she had just done. She had to know one thing – was Lisa alive or dead?

With the cold calculating calm of a professional hitman, she leant over and opened her rival's handbag and scrabbled through the contents of the bag until she found Lisa's make-up kit. She took out the tiny vanity mirror and held it up to Lisa's mouth for a few moments. No mist. Nothing. Then Lori pulled the engagement ring off Lisa's limp finger and put it in her pocket . . .

On August 24, 1990, Lori Esker was sentenced to life in prison for the murder of Lisa Cihaski. The judge at the court in Marathon County, Wisconsin recommended she serve at least 14 years.

Lisa's father Vilas Cihaski – referring to the first degree murder charge – said after the verdict: 'Lori always wanted to be number one and she got number one.'

The She Devil of Nancy

The sun had not yet risen above the fields of the picturesque village of Rosieres-aux-Salines. But the birds were already singing in the trees and the cattle were grazing peacefully on the green pastures that surrounded the sleepy hamlet.

The fruit trees in the garden of the white-washed cottage were carrying plentiful supplies of apples and pears that summer. Every now and again, a sparrow nestled its beak into a ripe piece of fruit, prompting it to drop to the ground where the insects feasted upon it.

A cock crowed from the distant farm across the fields, near the road where the cottage and a row of charming houses nestled neatly into the scenery.

That narrow route had the rather unnerving name of Ruelle de L'Abattoir – Slaughterhouse Lane. Livestock from miles around were taken there to be chopped up into slabs of meat for a hungry public.

But now the slaughterhouse was no more. Only the name remained. The smell of rotting carcasses was just a distant memory to some of the village's older residents.

When the sun rose above the vast plains on clear June mornings like this, the white-washed houses gave off a wonderful warm orange glow before shimmering brightly as the day wore on.

The orchard that belonged to the cottage was flanked by well kept gardens filled with blue pine, dwarf juniper and beds of hydrangeas and zinnias.

Inside the house, Madame Simone Weber was stirred by the shrill of her alarm. It was 4.15am and she had a vital appointment to keep.

In fact she never really needed to bother with an alarm clock. For there had not been a day in her entire life when she did not wake up before it actually went off.

It was hardly surprising really. Madame Weber was a tense, highly strung woman of fifty six. She had seen much suffering during her life. Perhaps her soul wanted to make sure she never failed to rise each morning? At least that's what she told herself.

Madame Weber was a small, lumpy woman with watery eyes that stuck out from a gaunt face. Her mouth was tight and hard with lips that looked like they hadn't received, or given, much love. A demeanour that did little to endear her to others. And yet, as the early morning puffiness around Madame Weber's eyes subsided, there was a hint of attractiveness about her. Something she used to her great advantage whenever she came across a possible suitor.

By 4.30am she was up and dressed in a white blouse and tweed skirt. It was an image that cut a respectable figure among the other residents of the village.

She looked out of the window at her garden. A beautiful sight in the low, golden sun.

But the splendour of the scene made no impression on Madame Weber. Her only concern was that appointment. It was a vital liaison. More important than any meeting she had ever planned in her entire life. She could not be late – no matter what.

As she got into her tiny green Citroen and started the engine, she didn't even notice the farmer from up the road waving good morning. He thought nothing of her rudeness. He was used to her strange behaviour and had come to accept it. In fact, he and the other locals preferred it that way. Most of them had refused to even ackowledge her existence after she inherited the house from her husband in 1980.

That might have seemed a heartless response – until you learned that she had only been married to eighty-year-old former gendarme Marcel Fixart for three weeks.

The marriage had scandalised the district. Local gossip had it that Madame Weber forced Fixart into a marriage he did not even realise had occurred.

The couple met through the lonely hearts column of a local newspaper. Madame Weber had once run a dating agency herself and knew just how vulnerable the people were who used their services.

Broke and virtually destitute, she decided that a brief relationship with an elderly man could be the answer to her problems.

She was only too well aware that her job at that time, as a washer woman, would hardly impress any prospective partner. So, before her first meeting with the old man, she bought herself a grey wig and renamed herself Monique Thuot – a retired professor of philosophy.

The relationship went slowly – far too slowly for Madame Weber's liking. She needed to marry Fixart to survive and he was reacting to her affections about as fast as a tortoise trying to climb the alps.

There was only one answer.

At the registry office in Strasbourg, it seemed like the fairy tale wedding of the elderly widower and the retired philosophy lecturer. But Fixart was back in Nancy – completely unaware of what was going on.

His place had been taken by aged retired actor Georges Hesling – paid a nominal sum by Madame Weber to act the part of Fixart.

It worked like a dream. To make matters even better both men died within weeks. No witnesses to the deception.

Fixart's family were outraged when they heard about the marriage *after* the old man's death. But there was nothing they could do about it.

Madame Weber's survival plan had worked. She inherited £10,000 and a beautiful cottage. It was only years later that the truth emerged.

Her mind was still only on one thing – that appointment.

Madame Weber's car slammed to a halt outside the gates of the battered looking factory on the edge of Nancy, none of the workers trouping in for the start of a hard day's work even looked up.

They were used to seeing the car. Madame Weber was a familiar face and they nearly all knew exactly what she was waiting for.

As the minutes passed by, she sat, looking more and more irritated in her car.

Just three yards away forty eight year old factory foreman Bernard Hettier cowered behind a wall wondering what he should do.

He could see the Citroen in the distance. But luckily Madame Weber hadn't spotted him.

Bernard was a good looking guy in a very French, older man sort of way. He still had a good head of sandy coloured hair and he was slim with craggy, almost rock-like features.

In recent months, he had been studiously trying to avoid Madame Weber. It was all his fault really. He should never have encouraged her into his bed in the first place. He should have known better. But his insatiable appetite for the opposite sex frequently led him into trouble.

Throughout two marriages, Bernard had found the lure of the flesh impossible to resist. He would often pick up vagrant women and seduce them before sending them packing. He loved them all alcoholics, drifters, lost souls.

Like the time, only a few weeks earlier, when he met a dark haired woman in a bar in Nancy. Bernard was sitting quietly sipping a beer when he caught her eye At first she just looked away, slightly embarrassed by the attention. But he persisted and eventually swaggered over to her table. Few words passed between them. But Bernard was determined to get his way. Fifteen minutes later, he walked out of the bar with the woman, who was in her late forties. He always preferred them a bit older. They were far less complicated than the young ones. In his experience, the older women were more carefree – less obsessed with actual love. More interested in lust.

Less than one hour later the pair emerged from the tiny pension and waved coldly goodbye to one another having just made love.

He had an astonishing record of success. It seemed

the Bernard Hettier school of charm really did work. And it was based on one simple theory: all women want to make love, whatever they might say at first. It was this principle that had attracted him to the distinctly unattractive Simone Weber in December, 1983.

She had called him after her lawn mower had broken down. A friend had recommended him highly. Madame Weber should have known how to fix it herself after her many years of experience as a car mechanic and restorer of old motors. But despite spending many hours tinkering with the engine, this lawn mower had her beaten – until Bernard appeared on the scene. Within minutes he got it going and was cutting the grass under the fruit trees in front of her cottage for the last time that winter.

For more than thirty minutes he trundled around the vast garden. She watched him fondly from a ground floor window as he did his job meticulously. Eternally grateful, she asked him in for a drink after all his efforts. It seemed only polite.

As she poured the bottle of beer for him, she felt a slight quiver in her stomach. Her hands shook with excitement. She couldn't take her eyes off him. He seemed so beautiful. Bernard sensed with his ever delicate nose that sex was in the air.

As the drink begun to work inhibitions and altering perspectives, he studied her bulbous features and they began to look beautiful in their own unusual way. He could feel himself beginning to fall for this plump, matronly creature. Fatter women are always more sexy, he thought. They've got more to offer. He felt sure she was thinking along the same lines.

Just one hour later Bernard and Madame Weber were making hot, passionate love in her bedroom upstairs. The relationship had begun.

Now, he was cowering behind a wall in the factory, watching and waiting. Unsure whether to face the woman, whose obsessive love became so unbearable that he broke the rule of a lifetime and ended an affair acrimoniously.

Bernard had always used his easy going nature and superb sense of humour to survive the onslaught of discarded women that littered his life.

He had such a relaxed attitude that it tended to rub off on his lovers. He was proud of the fact that even when he split with his lovers, it was always deemed by mutual agreement. Never acrimonious. Never nasty. Just civilised.

But then a lot of his women did not even know his full name, so it was not that difficult. Madame Weber was an exception to that rule – and it made Bernard feel uneasy. She also happened to know there was no other exit to that factory on that day. She was quite content to pass the time. Her lover was going to have to come through those gates – no matter what.

She seemed blissfully unaware that Bernard was a less than willing participant in this game of romance. He might have told her in no uncertain terms that it was over because he was seeing another woman, but she had steadfastly refused to accept the notion. She needed Bernard desperately. She longed for his body and his company. He made her feel young in a way no other man had ever done.

She was desperate for that pysical contact. The emotion. The touching. The sex.

'It's no good. I am going to have to face her,' thought Bernard to himself that morning.

He could not cower there for the rest of the day. He was exhausted from a gruelling ten hour night shift at the factory. And now *this*.

Bernard braced himself, took a deep breath walked towards the factory gate. He knew that Madame Weber would spot him within seconds but he steeled himself to look only dead ahead. 'She'll get the message if I don't look her in the eyes,' he thought. He couldn't have been more wrong.

Madame Weber was elated. There was Bernard. He looked tired but what did that matter? All she saw were his handsome features. There was a sensuous, warm feeling in her stomach. Like getting butterflies but far more forceful. She knew at that point she loved Bernard. Those were the vital signs.

Bernard sneaked a glance to his right to try and make out whether she had stirred from the Citroen. He didn't want to look her in the face.

He hesitated for a moment, taken aback with surprise. The car was empty. Where was she? Perhaps it wasn't her car? Relief flooded back into his body.

Suddenly, a hand grasped his from behind.
'Bernard. It's so good to see you. We must talk.'

His heart sank.

The tension returned instantly. Why couldn't she just leave him alone?

How could he get away from her? He was her emotional prisoner.

The worst part of it for Bernard was the temptation.

Months ago, he had wanted to get rid of this woman from his life forever. But now he was near her, he knew it would be virtually impossible to resist her. The physical need was always in him. Lurking. Just waiting for an opportunity. No matter how much he told himself he hated her, he wouldn't be able to stop himself.

But he truly wished she was not there in the first place.

So far, Bernard had responded with nothing more than a cursory 'Oh Hello.'

But that was enough. He had caved in. He had accepted her presence.

He was her captive. Emotionally and physically sometimes he would black out in her living room for no apparent reason. It would always happen just as he was about to leave after giving her the promised dose of passion she so actively pursued.

Bernard always wanted to get out of that house the moment they had completed the act. The feeling of guilt and disgust would sweep over him as she lay there in her layers of middle aged fat, looking longingly into his eyes. He would turn away in horror and promise himself, 'Never. Never again.' But he always came back for more.

After fainting, he would wake up in her bed and She would be nursing him back to health. Tending to him so lovingly. Spoon feeding him medicine she said would make him feel better. And he would be eternally in her debt. He couldn't just get up and walk out. It would be so rude so he'd stay there a little longer, duty bound to perform once more.

As if his dizzy spells weren't enough, he'd recently been plagued by regular lapses of memory. On a number of occasions he would completely forget arrangements that had been made after going out with Madame Weber.

Sometimes he would make love with her and find himself slipping into a trance-like state. Losing track of time and staying far too long in her company. His friends began to complain about his unreliability. Why was he always late after he had been with her?

He began to wonder whether she was doing something to him to ensure that he became her prisoner, whenever she wanted him. But it seemed a ludicrous notion. However, it got really serious when he started falling asleep at his desk in the factory. On one occasion, he was almost fired by his boss when he was discovered slumped over the bureau.

He went for tests at the local hospital and the doctors suggested he was perhaps being drugged by someone. At the time he hadn't really clicked. Who would want to do that? And why?

Now, as he stood outside the factory gates with the one women in the world he had no wish to ever see again, he reckoned he knew the answer.

'Let's go to your home. We must talk,' insisted Madame Weber.

Once again. Bernard didn't need to bother replying. This was an order not a request. There was no point in arguing.

As they drove the three miles to his modest home along twisting hedged-line lanes, he thought about the last time she had caught him outside the factory gates. How he had sworn he wouldn't let her cast her spell on him ever again.

That was a few weeks ago. And here he was, weak as ever.

As the couple pulled their cars up alongside the flat fronted house, all was still deadly quiet in the neighbourhood. It was still only 6.30 in the morning but in *preparation for the long day ahead* Bernard Hettler felt as if his day was over.

Inside the house, Madame Weber's warmness returned the feeling she had enjoyed so many times when they had been regular lovers. Before she had had to become much more forceful.

She remembered the love they had shared inside the slightly tatty bedroom with its worn, cream coloured walls. At first he had been so energetic, so innovative. He'd brought her to unbelievable peaks of ecstacy.

She made them both a cup of coffee while Bernard wondered to himself how he ever got himself into this messy affair. What on earth drove him to seduce this rolly poly shaped woman? And then expect to just walk away from the relationship. It was obvious she would come after him. How could she – the plain ex-nurse turned motor mechanic – accept that it was all over? She had nothing else. No-one to love her. *He* was alright. There were always women around for *him*. But she had no prospects of companionship other than him.

He should have thought of that when they met in her garden on that very first occasion.

Now, as they sat making difficult, almost stiff conversation, it finally dawned on Madame Weber that he was trying to get away from her for good.

There was a certain deadness about his responses

153

towards her. That wouldn't do. It wouldn't do at all. She must make sure there was no escape for him. He wasn't going to discard her like some used car. Not this time. It had happened to her so many times before.

She had put up with his philandering. The constant flow of other women. She even recalled the day she arrived at his house unexpectedly only to find him performing an unspeakable act. What hurt so much was that this with some waif and stray, another woman was even older than her.

Then again, it excited her to realise what a sexual animal he was.

Bernard was starting to feel slightly queasy. He presumed it was the fact he had been working all night was taking its toll.

He watched Madame Weber sitting opposite him at the coffee table but she was gradually slipping out of focus.

Then he blinked and his vision of her was cruelly sharp once more.

Her mouth spouted words that jabbed in the air. 'How's work going. Holiday. Holiday. You, *really*' They seemed like solid objects so that everytime they entered his head they bounced around him.

Then his brain awaiting recognition began to drop. Sleep gorgeous, welcoming sleep was all he need. He jerked it up again and just managed to recover consciousness.

He never woke up again.

Madame Weber had a lot of strength in her fat-enclosed

154

muscles. She'd acquired it through her work restoring and fixing vintage cars in her Nancy garage.

She needed every tiny bit of that power to help Bernard from her car to her sister's tiny apartment in the noisy Avenue de Strasbourg in the heart of the bustling city.

He wasn't conscious but somehow she managed to make him look like just another late afternoon drunk as she struggled up the stairs to their floor flat in the four-storey Victorian house.

She was driven by a hard determination to settle her love for this suburban style Don Juan once and for all. This was the ultimate test that she had to pass. It would be a true insight into how much she really cared for him.

Jean Haag and his wife Marie were both in their eighties and had been residents on the ground floor of that very same building for forty years. They knew Madame Weber and her sister Madeleine reasonably well in a neighbourly sort of way.

The Haags were very steeped in their own ways. They couldn't cope with new-fangled contraptions like television. But the pre-occupation that kept them alive more than anything else was a healthy inquisitiveness for all that went on around them. There wasn't a thing that went on in that house or the street outside, they didn't know about.

Frequently they would view the comings and goings from their front window, just by the only steps into the building, or peep through the spy-hole in their door if they heard anyone coming up or down the hallway.

They didn't need television. They had a round-the-clock live show featuring real people instead.

One of their favourite subjects was Madame Weber and her activities. She really intrigued them. Sometimes she would burst through the hallway doors late at night to stay the evening at the apartment. On other occasions she would spend entire days entertaining men friends above them and the Haags would listen, puzzled to the bumps and the squealings, it was a long time since they'd used a bed in that way.

They couldn't help noticing Madame Weber on that afternoon. After all, she did seem to be helping a rather drunken male friend into the house.

Madame Haag watched intently at the window while Weber struggled to find the key. Then her husband spied through the peep hole in their door as the couple slumped through the hallway.

They never saw him come down again.

Upstairs, Madame Weber was making a hell of a racket. Bernard now flat out on the floor of the living room. She felt his pulse. It was weak. She began tearing up black plastic bin liners and spreading them flat next to Bernard, tucking them under his back every now and then.

In the corner of the room lay a huge concrete cutter. It was a mean, unforgiving piece of hardware in every sense of the word. It seemed oddly out of place. In the room next door lay two .22 rifles, a silencer and three sticks of dynamite. She grimaced gleefully at the same.

This was the sweet climactic moment. Ever since he

156

had broken off what she saw as their engagement, she had been building up to it. She always hoped they could get together again. But she knew that it was not to be.

She kept thinking of how happy she had been when they were true lovers. Much happier than she had ever been before.

How she survived a first marriage that produced five children God only knows. Her husband had been a quiet, stoic man called Jaques Thuot. But his calmness was soon countered by the sheer dominance of Madame Weber.

It was a marriage that M. Thuot described as 'living hell.'

Not exactly helped by the fact that she got him committed to a mental hospital after pretending he had tried to kill her.

It was the ultimate revenge on a husband whose only sin was to seek a quiet life without the emotional upheaval that was a part of Madame Weber's staple diet.

When M. Thuot was committed to a real straitjacket environment it was, as he later explained, 'like going from one version of hell to another.'

And what of those five children? The unstable nature of her own life rubbed off on them with heartbreaking consequences. One daughter committed suicide in her teens. The reasons were never really uncovered. The son she so doted on was sent away to Germany on national service. He also took his own life – because he could not bear to be parted from the mother he so desperately loved.

That was before the farcical second marriage that was never consummated. Then along came Bernard. But he proved to be as bad as all the others. Actually, in many ways, he was even worse.

At least the others were faithful, if somewhat unlikely creatures.

Now she was planning a future where he would always be in her thoughts. If she could not have him then no-one else would get him.

She always knew she had it in her to kill. He had to prove it.

The saw turned slowly at first when she switched it on. But it rapidly gained such speed that it was impossible to make out the serrated edge of the blade.

The man in the equipment hire shop the previous morning had warned Madame Weber that the saw was really built for men to handle.

She was outraged. She had handled much larger bits of equipment over the years. How dare he suggest she wasn't fit for the job. She would show him.

Women are just as strong as men when they really want to be. Men always think they are supreme. They need to be taught a lesson.

But all the same she heeded his advice when he warned: 'It's very dangerous. Handle it with care, or it'll slice your finger off just like that.'

It sounded perfect.

Back in the flat, Madame Weber heaved up the heavy saw.

Protected by a brand new plastic fronted apron and

wearing skin tight black rubber gloves, she knelt down and tweaked the whirring blade against Bernard's flesh. It was surprising how little resistance it met.

The incision was sharp and precise. Her hand trembled with excitement before she swept the cutter across his chest. It was so easy, the blood burned as it met the hot metal while sealing the flesh as she went along. Soon he would be in nice square slabs. She'd be able to handle him quite easily then. Oh yes indeed . . .

Downstairs, the Haags could not help but notice the sound of what they presumed was one of those vacuum cleaners. It seemed a slightly strange noise for a vacuum cleaner to make. But what did they know?

Madame Weber was now beginning to appreciate why concrete block carving was considered by some to be an art form.

Every time she sliced into another portion of Bernard's body she felt an exquisite rush of adrenalin to her brain. The patterns she could make were so pretty. It was so *nice* of Bernard to continue to provide her with so much pleasure.

She had severed all his arms and legs from the torso with ease. It had been a bit like cutting up a chicken after it had been cooked. Now, she had to remove the head. That might be a little difficult? With the blade still whirring furiously she knelt down and held the throbbing machine over his jugular vein.

It had to be neat and tidy. Putting the body on plastic

bin liners had worked perfectly. It had prevented the blood from seeping through to the floor below.

As the blade sliced through the throat, she waited for the blood to spurt, but it just came out in a steady, manageable stream.

Within a minute the entire head had been decapitated. Her pudgy fingers grasped the head by its hair. It was remarkably heavy. For a second she feared she might drop it. But soon it was wrapped up safely in a heavy duty plastic bag. She had bought thirty of them at the same time as hiring the saw.

It was to hide the head from view. It was the one aspect of the dissection she had found faintly distasteful. But there was still work to do – a massive spring clean. She couldn't leave her sister's apartment in a mess. It would be *so* inconsiderate . . .

'You have got to help. We know he's in danger. This woman was very strange. He told us she always had a pistol with her, day and night.'

Bernard's sister Monique Goetz was frantic with concern for her missing brother as she stood in Nancy Police Station, pleading for help. Her appeal was falling on deaf ears. The police had heard it all before.

A self confessed romeo goes missing, leaving behind a long list of women he has loved and left.

'So what's new?' asked the cynical policemen behind the desk at the station.

Here was a man known for his sexual liaisons with hundreds of women and the police are supposed to sit up and take immediate action? He *knew* what had happened. Good old bonking Bernard Hettier

160

had arranged his own disappearance to start a new life somewhere else, probably with a new lover.

Back at the tiny flat, Madame Weber was stuggling out of the house with plastic bag after plastic bag. The Haags were fascinated. They had never seen so many bags left out for the rubbish collection in one go.

On the fifth load, Madame Weber felt a pang of panic when she noticed a gaping hole opening in the side of one bag. His head might fall out! She rushed to the bin just in time.

By the time the seventeenth and very last bag had been disposed of, Madame Weber felt a weird mixture of relief and exhaustion.

Inside the flat she opened up a suitcase Bernard had left at the flat many months previously, after one of their romantic interludes. It seemed the perfect place to to put his torso. In the end, in Madam Weber's eyes at least, he had brought about his own downfall. Now his own suitcase was going to carry his remains to their last resting place at the bottom of the River Marne. His remains would be weighted to the river bed by a slab of concrete from the garden he so lovingly mowed all that time ago. She wanted him to feel the full weight of her fury dragging him down, even after death.

Her sister Madeleine and her nephew had virtually volunteered their assistance in covering up his disappearance. They felt duty bound to help this poor, much maligned woman.

'He's gone away for a while. He doesn't want to be

bothered. He'll get in touch when he feels the time is right,' the male voice on the phone was hesitant, nervous.

On the other end of the line was Bernard's latest lover – the woman who had ultimately lured him away from Madame Weber. She was stunned. How could Bernard just get up and run away? They hadn't argued. There had been no hints of discord.

She felt angry and betrayed. His behaviour was outrageous. But, her friends told her, that was the sort of man she was dealing with.

The blurred voice, who described himself as Bernard's friend, was adamant. He would not be back for a long time. A very long time.

At the factory where he worked, the boss was hardly surprised to receive a Paris doctor's medical certificate stating that Bernard was too ill to work. Madame Weber's loyal nephew took care of that by posing as Bernard in the French capital city – a long way from Nancy. His stomach pains were so realistic, the doctor warned him to go to hospital if they persisted.

It might be some time before Bernard would be returning to work again.

At the equipment hire shop, the attendant was in a dismissive mood. Muttering to himself 'Typical woman. She goes and gets that concrete cutter stolen. She should never have hired it in the first place. It's a man's machine.'

Just moments earlier, Madame Weber had bitten her lip and held her temper after the man had mocked her when she returned to the shop to pay for the stolen item. She knew she shouldn't create a scene. She wanted her visit to that shop to be as low key as possible.

*   *   *

Madame Weber parked outside a row of garages near her sister's Villa in Cannes. This was where they would hide Bernard's rickety old car. Her sister, a dark haired version of herself in almost every way, pulled open the garage doors and Madame Weber drove the car straight into the opening.

As she slammed the garage doors shut she was overcome with re⌐ ⌐ef. Yet another part of that man's life had been locked away. Soon there would be nothing left of him in the entire world. The two sisters walked away and Madame Weber turned and warned Madeleine, 'We must be careful. People will be watching us. Listening to our every word.'

It proved to be a chillingly correct statement.

Back in Nancy, Bernard's family were very persistent. They wouldn't rest until an investigation was launched.

'He may have been a lady's man. But he wouldn't just disappear off the face of this earth. Something has happened to him. You have to help.'

Eventually, the police accepted that this was no everyday disappearance.

There was only one person the gendarmes could turn to – Judge Gilbert Thiel.

The bearded, bespectacled former lawyer was, under French law, the man who would have to head the investigation – and find out if there were any suspicious sides to the enquiry. His correct, formal title was Juge d'Instruction, or examining magistrate, a position with no equivalent in the British system of justice.

In principle, his duty was to gather all possible facts

163

relating to the matter in hand, weigh them with the proper objectivity and deploy his powers accordingly in deciding whether or not a case can proceed.

The appeals from the family were growing and Judge Thiel knew something had to be done – and quickly Bernard's sister Monique was adamant that Madame Weber was involved.

'It is completely within her powers. She is a strange woman. Mad enough to do it. I *know* she's involved.'

Judge Gilbert had a hunch she might be right. Whatever the situation, he had little else to go on, so he launched the investigation by ordering a phone tape on Weber and her sister Madeleine.

'Do you think we should find a new school for Bernadette?' Madame Weber was talking on the phone from her cottage to her sister in Cannes.

They weren't discussing a child as one might presume. They were talking about the car. It was their cryptic code word for it. The 'school' was the garage.

Madame Weber was worried. She had heard strange clicking sounds on her phones for weeks.

She was pretty sure she was under surveillance but she had no hard and fast evidence.

Then she got a phone call from the estate agent who rented her the garage.

'Mme Chevalier. Do you wish to renew this monthly agreement,' he asked.

The officers listening to this were intrigued. Suddenly,

some of those missing pieces of the jigsaw were starting to come together.

Judge Thiel and his officers soon traced the garage to Mme Chevalier. Weber had been using a false name and they were on to something. Anybody who uses a false name has something to hide.

The garage door was not difficult to force. The Cannes police were somewhat bewildered by the request of their colleagues in Nancy, but they understood it was a murder investigation so they co-operated.

Inside the tatty lock-up they found Bernard's Renault 4. Now Thiel was beginning to understand Weber's cryptic telephone conversations.

But the car in itself was not enough to prove Madame Weber was involved in the murder of Bernard. They needed more evidence. Much more.

For she had a left an intricate trail of deception across France in a desperate bid to avoid implication.

Judge Thiel was stunned. He had just burst into the tiny apartment on the Avenue De Strasbourg hoping to find some traces of human flesh or maybe even some blood on the floor. Instead he had found nothing to connect Madame Weber with Bernard Hettier's mysterious disappearance.

Then, as the officers casually looked in the room next door, they uncovered an arson that more befitted the safe house of an international terrorist than a grandmotherly widow. He was staring straight into the barrels of two .22 rifles, a silencer, three sticks of dynamite in an old handbag and in a casserole pot in the kitchen, 40 rubber stamps stolen from town halls, local government offices and chemists' shops.

It was an astounding haul – and it put matters in a completely different perspective.

But he still had found no trace of a body.

The children playing on the edge of the River Marne, just south of Paris, thought it was their lucky day. They had spotted a suitcase washed up on the bank and were trying to open it.

They didn't bother to think why a breeze block was attached to the handle in order to make it sink without trace. And they wouldn't have known that the blue dab of paint on the stone was the same colour and brand as the freshly painted blue gable of that cottage in Slaughterhouse Lane.

As they grappled with the lock to try and force it open, a man walking on the river bank waved them away. He instantly knew that this was not hidden treasure.

The policeman who eventually forced open the case vomitted on the spot. Inside was a torso without head, arms, or legs. In Nancy, Judge Thiel reckoned he had the body of Bernard Hettler.

On November 8, 1985, he and three officers turned up at the white-washed cottage in Rosieres-aux-Salines and arrested Simone Weber.

For more than five years – the longest period of remand ever instituted – Madame Weber was kept in custody without facing her accusers as Judge Thiel continued, some said obsessively, to gather evidence that would conclusively prove the crimes she had committed.

On March 1, 1991, Simone Weber, by now aged 60, was found guilty of the brutal murder of her lover Bernard Hettier and sentenced to 20 years in prison.

In one of the most sensational trials in French legal history she was also aquitted of the murder of her second husband Marcel Fixard for lack of evidence.

The newspapers labelled her *The She-Devil of Nancy and it stuck*.

Help me Somebody . . .
Please?

Shopping malls are a virtual institution throughout the United States of America. They are vast spreads of stores all in one place with just one car park. Very convenient. Very cosy. Very safe.

The idea behind them is that shoppers can get everything they want in one place. It saves time – and time is money.

The Puente Hills Mall, in California's San Gabriel Valley was a typical example. Despite being just 25 miles from the centre of sprawling, glamorous Los Angeles it could have been one of a thousand such malls stretched across the nation.

At any one moment there would be hundreds of vehicles parked in the vast car park in front of the main entrance to the Puente Hills Mall. Mothers with their children. Husbands with their wives. Grandparents with their grandchildren. Every cross section of the local population. The rich. The not so rich. The poor. The not so poor. They all had one thing in common – a need to shop, a need to buy – and Puente Hills was the perfect location.

Besides every type of store, there were banks, estate agents, restaurants and, naturally, a MacDonalds. Basically, shopping malls like the one at Puente Hills were the classic example of the American Dream.

Stores competed with each other to keep prices rock bottom. Huge advertising hoardings blared out at you the moment you drove into the car park. It was a place where you could spend all your hard earned cash, but still feel you were getting good value for money.

Robbin Machuca, Eileen Huber and John Lewis looked every inch the products of that American Dream as they sat in Eileen's brown Mercury car at the Mall on August 27, 1991.

Robbin and John were half-brother and sister. Her darker skin contrasting with the lighter brown features of Lewis. Eileen was caucasian – the product of a one-parent middle class family in a cosy nearby suburb. But the racial mix of the group hardly raised an eyebrow in the mall on that day. This was not the Deep South in the 1930s. This was California in 1991 – blacks and whites had long since learned to befriend each other without fear of retribution.

But then you wouldn't think so if you met Eileen's father Gary. He was known as 'John Wayne' in the neighbourhood where they lived because of his vast collection of guns. But, other less kind souls, called him 'White Trash' or 'Redneck' because he still hinted at believing in white supremacy.

Though overpowering, his attitudes had not rubbed off on 20 year old Eileen. Her fiancé John was black and she was proud of it. Maybe she was also secretly quite pleased that her father so disapproved.

Eileen loved being in the company of John and Robbin. They had such a laid back attitude towards life. 'Live for the day for tomorrow may never come.' They worshipped that famous line written by Jimi Hendrix. It encompassed their feelings about the world.

You see, so many tragedies had already befallen John, aged 21, and Robbin, aged 26. Their lives were a like web of endless disasters. One outrage leading to the next. Long ago, their American Dream had turned into an American Nightmare. John's mother was an alcoholic. His father a pimp shot to death on the mean streets of South Central Los Angeles when he was a baby.

As a small boy he would throw rocks at the family's German Shepherd dog until one day the dog broke its chain and mauled him viciously. At just eight years of age, he was arrested for armed robbery. By the time he was 10, he was in a juvenile detention centre. Then he joined one of the city's most notorious gangs – the Westside Bloods. It was his escape from anonimity. Now he was a person in his own right. He had an identity at last. A reputation as a cruel, violent gang member. But at least they knew who he was.

Then he met Eileen Huber.

John's half sister Robbin could give a pretty similar account of her background. Her father was an American Indian in jail for armed robbery when she was born. At 12 years of age, she became pregnant by her stepfather. Confused and afraid she denied it at first. Even as the doctor delivered the baby, she told her stepfather: 'You're lyin. You cannot be the father.' But he knew it was true.

A few months later, Robbin's stepfather confessed his evil deed to his wife. He handed her mother a gun and ordered her to shoot them all. Her mother refused. But, to her daughter's eyes, she committed the ultimate act of betrayal by refusing to kick her husband out of that house. Bitter and hysterical, Robbin grabbed

170

the baby and jumped out of the back window of their home. She never came back. She joined the gangs. She did hundreds of burglaries. At 15 she got jailed. It was a blessing in disguise. At last, Robbin had a place to rest her head. A place to learn. She was taught secretarial skills. On her release she got a job in a mortgage company. Her probation officer was convinced she had escaped her tragic background and could start afresh. Robbin seemed happy. But then there came a turning point. Her apartment was wrecked by burglars in just the same sort of crime she used to commit. She could not cope with the losses. Robbin quickly returned to her old, familiar ways.

It all made Eileen's family history pale into insignificance. Until very recently she had lived in the same house all her life. Even her freckle-faced strawberry blonde looks had hardly altered since early childhood. She was so skinny they used to call her Olive Oyl, after Popeye's girlfriend.

All the other kids used to love going around to her house because it was like an Aladdin's cave of film star fantasy. On the lounge walls were posters of John Wayne, her father's hero. But Eileen's room was like a shrine to her favourite idol Lucille Ball. When people walked in, they felt they were entering a time warp back to the fifties. Pictures of the blonde comedian adorned every inch of wall space. She'd always loved Lucy. They used to say she was just like her. And that made Eileen feel good. On the book shelves were videos of every movie Lucille Ball ever made. They were crammed between countless novels with titles like *Miss Teen Sweet Valley*.

But Eileen started to question her life just a year

earlier. She had begun to wonder what future lay ahead. The outlook was bleak. It felt empty and meaningless. Written in red felt tip pen on the wall above the headboard of her bed was a nagging piece of graffiti dated July 25, 1990. 'What's come over you?' The adolescent scrawl begged. 'Help me somebody . . . please.'

Eileen's father Gary never even bothered to read it.

Now these three desperate people seemed to be putting on a brave face as they laughed and smiled whilst chatting between mouthfuls of tasty Chinese food in the Puente Hills Mall on that day in August, 1991.

'Don't you care about anything?'
Eileen was laughing as she uttered those words. But there was a serious undercurrent to what she was asking her friend Robbin.

'I'd rather not care than care 'cuz then you get hurt.' Robbin's reply summed it all up really. She was dead inside. She had felt like that for so long she reckoned there was nothing left to lose. Life had dealt far too many blows in her direction. What could she possibly owe to anyone? No-one had given her anything but pain. To care would be like paying back a debt that she didn't owe . . .

Just a mile away at the Lynx Golf company, 56-year-old Shirley Denogean was leaving her firm's offices for her lunch break. She usually bought a sandwich at one of the nearby cafes but on this particular day she had to buy a birthday card for a relative.

172

The easiest place to find one was at the Puente Hills Shopping Mall. And Shirley was a regular at the Mall – it was her favourite place to hunt for bargains. In any case, it was a beautiful hot sunny day in the San Gabriel Valley. Perfect for a short drive.

As Shirley turned on the ignition of her silver 1980 Mercedes, her only thoughts were on buying that card and getting back to work on time. She did not want to upset her bosses by taking an extra long lunchbreak.

At first the car did not start. But then it was always doing that. Shirley tried again. This time the vast V-8 engine came to life. If only it hadn't.

'She's perfect.'

John Lewis spat out the words between heaps of Chinese food stuffed in his mouth. All three of them were watching Shirley Denogean driving her Mercedes into the parking lot at the Puente Hills Shopping Mall.

'Let's wait until she comes back.'

The two women giggled nervously in anticipation as Lewis barked his order at them. They all knew what was about to happen. This wasn't the first time.

Inside the greetings card shop, Shirley looked at her watch slightly anxiously. The drive had taken longer than she expected. She had to be back at the office in a few minutes. After paying the cashier, she walked briskly back to her gleaming, spotless car. There was no time to waste. In her haste, she did not see Lewis and the two women approach. There were so many people around that day. There was nothing unusual about a black couple and a white girl. Why should she notice them?

'Get in the fucking car – now!'

Shirley Denogean felt a sharp stabbing pain as the

173

barrel of Lewis' gun prodded deep into her back. For a split second she felt annoyed that anyone should come anywhere near her. How dare they? They must have made a mistake. This could not be happening to her surely?

But the reality of the situation rapidly dawned on Shirley when she turned around and saw the blank, emotionless faces of her assailants and then looked down and saw the gun pointing towards her.

'I said, in the car bitch!'

This time Shirley did exactly what she was told. She felt her stomach tighten inside, like somebody had grabbed it then twisted. She wanted to heave through fear, but there was absolutely nothing she could do. To anyone walking by, it would have seemed like a perfectly ordinary scene. Four people sitting in a saloon car about to drive off. If they had looked more closely, they would have seen the horror on the face of Shirley Denogean. They would have sensed the robber's adrenalin pumping, seen the pupils in the eyes dilating through nervous excitement.

'What do you want? Have anything.'

Shirley began ripping open her purse. Cash and credit cards cascaded onto the floor of the Mercedes. She looked at the faces of those two women. She wondered how they could do this. She understood a man but not the women? Surely they must feel some empathy for another female? But there was nothing there for Shirley to grasp at. Robbin and Eileen had done this before. This was just another 'job' – they would not have even known what the word empathy meant. She had money and that was all that mattered.

'Give me the fucking number NOW! Or we'll kill you mother fucker.'

Lewis grasped hold of the bank cash card and yelled at Shirley. He seemed out of control. Almost on a terror trip. His head felt filled with blank spaces. There was no feeling. There was no sorrow. There was no pity. He just wanted the password for that card so he could steal her money.

Shirley watched helplessly as Eileen Huber walked off towards the ATM machine just a few yards from where they were parked. Beside her in the back seat of her own Mercedes was Robbin Manchuca. In front, Lewis. She wanted to scream her head off to alert one of the hundreds of people walking nearby. But she feared they might use that gun if she so much as uttered a word out of place.

This was a battle for survival for Shirley. And pride. Your dignity is the first thing that goes when fear grips you and won't let go. She tried to remain calm but the tears of terror were welling up in her eyes. She felt close to bursting point. But she wasn't going to let them get her. She had to be hard. She did not want to show them her emotions. That would give them instant victory. She did not want them to win.

Shirley looked closely at Robbin. She had an attractive, almost soft face. How could this woman even contemplate the crimes they were participating in? Surely they would not kill her? Not two women? There had to be some mercy there. There had to be some understanding.

By the time Eileen returned from the cash dispenser,

the atmosphere had relaxed somewhat. Few words had been exchanged between any of those people in that car.

But something was about to happen. She could sense it. Her hands were sticky with sweat. She felt the silence on them and the air was so thick she could hardly breath

Robbin stepped out of the Mercedes after Eileen got back in. What was happening? Perhaps they were going to leave her now? Shirley prayed that this was the end of her nightmare. Tragically, it had only just begun.

Lewis started up the car. Just like earlier it did not turn over first time. For the first time in her life Shirley wished her car would conk out completely. Behind them, Robbin had started Eileen's Mercury first time. She waited for her step-brother and his fiancée to get going. After a few agonising seconds, the Mercedes roared into life.

Then followed a bizarre trip around all the cash dispensers that existed in Puente Hills Shopping Mall. Each time Lewis spotted one he would carefully pull the car to a halt in a parking space and prod the barrel of his revolver into Shirley's side.

'What's the number for this fucking card? What is it?' Shirley had a lot of cash cards in her purse that day – it was like a windfall to Lewis and the two women.

Robbin's boyfriend Vincent Hubbard had been absolutely right when they had discussed a good way of making fast bucks.

'Hit the cash dispensers man,' he'd said. 'It's fucking

easier than holding up liquor stores. Fewer witnesses. Less problems.'

Hubbard would have been there with them that day if he hadn't volunteered to stay home with Robbin's five year old daughter. But then Hubbard should have known. He had just got out of jail after serving time for everything from robbery to drugs. Cash card dispenser hold-ups were the talk of the cells in the LA County Prison.

Now Lewis, Robbin and Eileen were cleaning up as much cash as they could from Shirley Denogean's credit cards. It was a horrific ride for her. The longer it went on the more certain she was that they were going to kill her. The more money they got the more brazen they became. By the time, they had taken cash out of a sixth machine, Lewis and the two women were positively oozing excitement.

'This is fucking great. We won't have to do another job for weeks.'

Lewis was ecstatic. All this cash was like a gift from God.

'Hey John. We're goin' to have ourselves a real good time.'

Eileen was looking forward to a few weeks without the usual money problems. Robbin – following behind in the Mercury – was happy too. None of them gave a moment's thought to the terrified middle-aged woman they had just kidnapped on a ride to Hell.

They had run out of cash dispensing machines. Now this horrible convoy of death was about to begin its final journey.

'Let's head for the freeway.'

Lewis knew that the nearby motorway was the best

route out of the Puente Hills Shopping Mall. If anything did go wrong then they could be away and on the main road in seconds. Shirley Denogean knew what it meant as well. She was convinced it meant the beginning of the end of her life.

'Go ahead. Kill me now.'

Lewis looked around the moment he heard Shirley utter those words.

'What the fuck . . . ? Shut the fuck up will ya?'

Eileen looked away almost embarrassed by their captive's outburst and her lover's reply. But it was only a momentary lapse – she worshipped the very ground John Lewis walked on. She could see no evil in his ways. She did not even stop to think that anything he had done was wrong. He was the man she loved. The man she was going to marry. The man whose baby she thought she might be expecting. The man with so many bloody victims. The man who did not care about anything other than her. She remembered how – just a few days earlier – Lewis had given her a beautiful sapphire ring to celebrate their engagement.

'There you go sugar. Now we are one.'

It was the first time Eileen had ever been given anything in the name of love. She looked at the well crafted ring and ran her finger tips across the smooth stone. She did not ask where he got it from. She already knew. But she did not care. She did not care that he had taken it from the corpse of one of his victims. She had been a woman very much like Shirley Denogean. Same sort of age. Same sort of dress. In fact they had robbed and killed her after kidnapping her at the Puente Hills Mall as well. That Mall was supposed to be the prime example of safe shopping for a safe society. John Lewis,

178

Robbin Machuca, Eileen Huber and Vincent Hubbard had made sure that all those illusions had been well and truly shattered.

'I said go ahead and kill me *now*.'

Shirley Denogean shouted the last word at the top of her voice and smashed her fist down on Lewis' neck and tried to grab the gun out of his lap.

For a few wild moments, he lost control of the car and it skidded across two lanes of the Pomona Freeway. Luckily there was no traffic nearby. Shirley must have wished there had been. Then, at least she might have stood a chance of surviving this living nightmare.

Lewis was furious. His empty emotionless behaviour had been replaced by a fit of temper that was truly terrifying.

He swung his fist across Shirley's face.

'Shut up you fucking bitch.'

The atmosphere inside the Mercedes was now unbelievable. But Shirley was not sobbing. She was angry. Angrier than she had ever been before in her entire life. She was not going to die easily. If they wanted to kill her they had better get a move on because she was going to fight them all the way. Behind the Mercedes, Robbin was apprehensive. She did not care about that woman. But she did worry about her brother and Eileen. They had almost got themselves killed a few seconds earlier. They had to get rid of that piece of trash. Robbin considered Shirley to be just another victim – nothing more or less. She had no feelings about her. But then people she had been much closer to during her own painful life had not cared about her. She thought about her step-father.

179

The so called, loving father figure who crept into her bed at nights and raped her. She thought about her mother. The one person in the world who should have loved and protected her. Instead, she allowed that animal to carry on his attacks unhindered. Never once did she step in and stop those brutal sex attacks. Not once.

Robbin didn't care about Shirley Denogean. Why should she? Human decency had long ago ceased to exist in her life.

'Go on. Go ahead and kill me.'

Lewis couldn't stand this woman a moment longer. Why didn't she just shut up? Why was she making it all so fucking painful? Shirley knew this was her only opportunity. She had to harass and hinder them as much as possible. Then she might stand a chance. Her instincts would not allow her to give up the fight. She wanted to live.

But all she was actually doing was forcing Lewis and Eileen to face a situation they had already dealt with on at least three previous occasions. They saw themselves as latter day Bonny and Clydes. Rightfully taking what they felt was theirs. Shirley was making a nuisance of herself. Her time had come. Lewis pulled the Mercedes over onto the hard shoulder of the freeway. Just a few yards behind, Robbin came to a halt in Eileen's Mercury.

'I am not getting out. You'll have to kill me first.'

Shirley just would not give in. She knew they would never shoot her there in front of all those passing motorists. If she refused to budge maybe, just maybe, she still stood a chance.

180

But Lewis was not going to let Shirley stand in his way. He lent into the back of the car and pulled the grandmother out of the seat of her own Mercedes. This was just another one to Lewis. Another face. Another day. Another victim. When Shirley Denogean looked into Lewis' eyes at that moment she knew he did not care. She knew that her death sentence was already confirmed.

At gunpoint, he made her walk along the side of the freeway towards an embankment. Just behind, Eileen and Robbin followed. They knew what was about to happen. They had seen it all before. But Robbin did not flinch when Eileen stopped walking and hung back so as not to see what was about to happen.

'Lie down.'

Shirley did not flinch despite the order from Lewis.

'I said fucking lie down – bitch.'

Shirley Denogean was not about to lose her dignity after all this time. She turned and looked into Lewis' eyes. He tried to avert her gaze. He felt uncomfortable. He hated the way she was looking at him. He felt challenged. But he also felt uneasy. She would not lie down and let him shoot her in the back. She was still looking straight at him. He couldn't handle it. This was not the way it was with the others. He could not shoot into her face and look at those eyes staring at him.

He aimed the revolver at her stomach and pulled the trigger. Whether he hoped to kill her or just injure her we will never know. Shirley fell to the ground instantly. She clutched her stomach but she was still very much alive. Lewis turned and walked away. He could not stand to look at her a moment longer. He did not care if she lived or died but he could not bear to see those eyes again.

'Bastard. You bastard.'

Shirley wanted him to know. She wanted him to realise what he had actually just done. Lewis could not stand the noise of her screaming.

He turned around, walked back towards her and lifted his gun. This time he pulled the trigger again and again and again. Each time a shot rang out he saw her body jerk with the force of the bullet as it entered.

The first shot entered her shoulder and split open a gaping wound. Bits of flesh flew upwards.

The next bullet ripped into the side of her body. But still Shirley fought back.

'Bastard. Bastard. Bastard.'

'Why don't you shut the fuck up bitch?'

Lewis aimed at the head this time. That shut her yapping. He hated the noise. He hated the screaming. It reminded him of reform school when the kids yelled so loudly in the playground before they beat him up. But worst of all, it reminded him of his perverted stepfather and how he would shout at him in fury before forcing him onto the bed.

'SHUT UP! SHUT UP! SHUT UP! SHUT UP!'

With each word he fired again and again. John Lewis had to get all those dreadful memories out of his mind for ever.

Peppering a twitching, innocent human being was a therapeutic way of cleansing his soul. When it was all over he looked up and saw his half sister Robbin looking down at him. She smiled. She approved. They had nothing to lose.

* * *

Lewis, Machuca, Hubbard and Huber were arrested in September 1991 after detectives identified them from security photographs taken by one of the cash dispenser machines. An alert shop keeper also took the registration number of Eileen's Mercury when they tried to use some of their stolen credit cards in a clothes store.

All four are accused of at least four similar random killings that terrorised the residents of the San Gabriel Valley in August 1991.

If found guilty they all face the death penalty.

The Scapegoat

Sara Thornton threw the newspaper on the bed of her cell in a fury. She could not believe what she had just read. How could they? How could they? How could they free a man who admitted killing his wife?

She was serving a life sentence for an identical crime. The only difference was that she was a woman and her victim was a man.

Sara had been locked up inside Her Majesty's Prison *Bullwood Hall*, in Essex, for almost 18 months. Her appeal against her sentence had just been turned down. Yet Joseph McGrail had kicked his frail wife to death and been allowed his liberty. It all seemed so unjust. So unfair. So inconsistent.

Sara faced a near lifetime in prison while Joseph McGrail had walked to freedom from the very same Birmingham Crown Court where she had received her sentence. That made it even worse somehow. The inconsistency of the law was one thing, but when the same court handed out two such entirely different punishments for basically the same crime it was a cruel double blow.

As she walked the jail corridors towards the refectory that afternoon she could not see or feel anything. Her mind was asking over and over again. Why? Why? Why?

'Hello Sara.'

Her fellow inmates might as well not have existed.

184

She did not hear them when they greeted her. They knew something must be wrong but they did not like to ask. The killers often got depressed. Who wouldn't if they faced half their life behind bars?

Sara took a small bowl from the pile of plates at the beginning of the food counter in the prison kitchen. She glanced past the hot, steaming overcooked meat. The broiled vegetables. The stinking fish. She stopped at the salad bar and picked at the lettuce, tomatoes and cucumbers on offer. They hardly looked appetising, but then Sara Thornton did not feel particularly hungry.

She looked at the rows of inmates sitting at the long refectory tables and realised she could not face a conversation with any of them. The strain of prison small talk was bad enough at the best of times, but she could not get her mind off Joseph McGrail. She did not even know the man. Not even what he looked like. But her thoughts were consumed by him. Why did he get freed when she was rotting in jail for an identical crime? Maybe he bribed the judge? Perhaps he begged for mercy? No. None of those reasons seemed entirely plausible. There was only one answer. It was because he was a man. That had to be the reason. What else could it possibly be?

Sara found herself just standing there with the salad bowl in her hand staring into oblivion.

'Are you sitting down or what?'

She snapped out of her self-induced trance the moment she heard that voice. It helped her decide. There was little pity between the four walls of a prison. Sara made up her mind there and then to do something about it. She wanted the world to know how unfair her sentence was. She walked back

185

to her cell with that bowl of salad still gripped in one hand.

A few minutes later, she heard the ominous clank of her cell door locking. It was the beginning of the end of yet another horrible day.

As Sara lay on the wafer thin mattress of her cast iron bed, she started to cry. It was controllable at first. But then she just let the emotion take over. The earlier tension was being replaced by floods of fear and anxiety. There was now no light at the end of her tunnel. No hope for an early release from this hell on earth.

No-one else did anything to try and console Sara that night as she sobbed into her pillow. She had no-one to turn to except herself, inside that grim, soul-less place. Now she had run out of giving herself reassurance. There was nothing left.

On her bedside table, that bowl of salad lay untouched. Sara's appetite for all things had disappeared. She looked at the bowl for a moment and then sent it crashing to the cold stone floor. She decided there was one last way to force them to change their minds.

'It's your life Sara.'

The prison officer in charge of her block was not unsympathetic to Sara's plight. But when she announced she would be going on hunger strike in protest against her sentence it merely provoked a sigh of acceptance from prison staff members. After all, they had seen it all before.

Their main aim was to keep the inmates alive and healthy with the minimum of fuss. This was just another problem as far as they were concerned. And it was a problem they could have done without.

Back in her cell, Sara felt a fresh surge of energy. She had inspired herself by deciding to refuse food from then on. Now she had an aim in life – even though it could lead to her death.

A few days later, sitting at the tiny desk in her eight foot by eight foot cell, she started to write a letter to her 12-year-old daughter. The daughter she had been forced apart from 18 months earlier. The daughter she loved and cherished like no other human being. The daughter she so desperately wanted to see again.

Hello Darling,

It is Sunday morning. I feel fine, a little weak I guess. You do make me laugh when I tell you I am going on hunger strike, you tell me to take care of myself. Perhaps you don't quite understand. Either they let me free, or I will die. It is that simple, there are no alternatives.

I think I am forcing people to examine their own commitments to their lives. Just how many people know that things are wrong yet always find excuses not to do anything simply because it is the easier thing to go with the flow?

I feel weak, tired and bone cold but my spirit is strong.

My skin is drying out. I'm going to end up just as one big wrinkle.

Sara Thornton put the pen down to rest a while. Her wrist ached from the pain of those words. She stretched and rolled her fingers to warm them against the cold. Then she shut her eyes and thought back to life in the outside world. Was it really that good?

*　*　*

Sara had felt something special toward Malcolm Thornton the first moment she had met him. He was such a nice bloke. Nothing was too much trouble for him. He'd been a policeman once. An upholder of the law. Sara was convinced that made him a fine, upstanding person. A man who could be trusted.

Malcolm was such a contrast from her earlier disastrous relationships. She was ecstatic when he asked her to marry him. She did not hesitate.

Their home in the picture postcard town of Atherstone, Warwickshire, looked like the perfect place for peace and harmony. But then appearances can be deceptive.

'You've got to come quickly doctor. I think he's going to kill me.'

Sara Thornton had been married to Malcolm for just a few weeks. Now she was at her wit's end. Her fine, upstanding husband was not just drunk. He was absolutely paralytic. As she put the phone down she turned to face the mounting fury of her beast of a husband. The very same man who had just a few weeks earlier promised to love and cherish her for the rest of his life was now smashing furniture to pieces. His eyes flared up in an alcoholic blurt when he spotted Sara. He had finished with the furniture. Now it was her turn.

When Dr Kenneth Farn got to the Thornton house on that hot summer's day in July, 1988, he was shocked. Sara was shaking with fear as the drunken lout who called himself her husband lay on the floor of their lounge gurgling and slurping uncontrollably. He looked like a beached whale. His time would come. His time would come.

'You have to sort yourself out Malcolm. You need treatment.'

Malcolm Thornton knew the doctor was right. But then he was sober now. You see, there were two Malcolm Thorntons. One was a funny, bright, witty man who would bowl people over with his generosity. The other Malcolm was like a raging wild animal destroying everything and everyone in his path. Sara Thornton knew both of them. She wished she did not.

But now the charming, reasonable Malcolm was facing up to the facts like a true man. He was an alcoholic and he accepted the fact. Dr Farn wanted to help his patient. Malcolm took his advice and headed for a specialist in London. Sara sighed with relief. He was doing something about it. He was a good man. He would sort himself out. She really wanted the loving, sweet Malcolm back forever.

By Christmas, 1988, Sara really thought she had got him back. 'Mr Hyde' had been beaten back into a shadowy past. And there, she was. The treatment had worked wonders. He was like a different man. She was so happy. So was her daughter Louise, aged 10. She wanted her mother to have the best in life. She deserved it.

Sara really felt true love for him. She had a reason to get up in the mornings. It felt so good to be so content. But it didn't last. It never does when you are dealing with the Malcolms of this world. There is always something lurking beneath the surface. That's why he had taken to the drink in the first place. There was a hidden motive behind his madness. Somewhere in there was a tortured soul desperate to get out. Alcohol was the only way it could manifest itself. It was his release from endless emotional torture. He could not hold it back for ever. Malcolm Thornton was the only person who really understood that.

'He's trying to kill me doctor. You've got to do something.'

Dr Farn was not surprised when he picked up the phone and Sara Thornton was on the line once more. In more than forty years as a GP, Malcolm Thornton was not the only alcoholic he had come across. Nevertheless, Dr Farn was still very concerned. His priority was the health and safety of Sara and Louise. He did not want to have a battered family on his conscience. Now he had a duty to protect his patients.

At the other end of the line, all hell was breaking loose in that pretty little house in the pretty little street in that pretty little town.

'Bitch. Uhm gunnuh kill you.'

Malcolm Thornton could barely speak the words coherently. But she knew exactly what he was saying. He was raving drunk. Completely out of control. He could have done anything to her. He didn't care.

But she still did not see his right hand clenching into a fist as his fury mounted. The first Sara knew about it was when she felt the knuckles crunch into her ribs. It was agonising. He had put his full, drunken force behind the punch and hit whatever he could focus on. It was easier than trying to aim at her face.

Thornton stumbled as he threw the punch into her

190

stomach. It just made it worse. His full weight was behind it. There was no way to stop the double impact as his fist connected.

Sara doubled up in pain and collapsed to the floor of their lounge, clutching her stomach. It felt as if she had been turned inside out. She tried to push her stomach muscles outwards. The pain was appalling. The internal bruises had already begun.

He stood over her glaring, ready to follow up his assault with a flurry of punches. But there was no need. Sara would never recover.

'I want to kill him. I hate him.'

Sara Thornton knew she shouldn't have said it the moment she saw the reaction on her friend's face. She had spoken her mind once too often. Now was not the time to tell someone her feelings about her husband. It was better to keep everything bottled up inside herself. That way the hatred could fester and fester until she reached a point of no return. Pouring your problems out was too easy an answer to Sara's anguish. If she could rid herself of the hatred and fear just by telling a friend her innermost thoughts then life would be simple wouldn't it?

No. Society much preferred you to keep it all locked inside your brain. Never let it out to anyone. That way we might never know what awful thoughts you have. Basically, most people do not want to know what their friends are really thinking. It might be embarrassing. It might be shocking. It might be the *truth*.

As Sara quickly changed the subject following her candid disclosure, she realised that Malcolm Thornton was a problem she was going to have to sort out on her own. No-one was going to help her. She would have to do it alone.

Malcolm Thornton's life was already falling apart without any assistance from his wife. He had lost his job after being breathalised. He had gone on a drinking spree following his release by the police. He had assaulted his wife. He had battered himself into submission.

What else did he have left in his life other than alcohol? It was his easiest form of escape. When the drink began to take effect he felt a surge of relief. He knew he could forget all his problems for a few hours and just soak himself in the dull throb of alcohol. The mortgage payments. The wife. No job. No future. Who gave a fuck? All those thoughts were left behind while he lapped up the beers and spirits that had become his staple diet in life.

The pubs were like a separate world for Malcolm Thornton. No-one bothered him. He could talk to who he liked when he liked. If he wanted to sit in the corner and sup silently he could. If he wanted to talk to his drinking partners about football and women he could. It was his choice. It was his way out.

Meanwhile at home, Sara was at the end of her tether. Her husband – the man whom she so adored when they married just a few months earlier – had now become an out and out failure. No job. No income. No love. No life. And no future for them.

He had put paid to that and she hated him for it. How could he destroy everything around him?

It was all such a waste.

She sat and watched the television but she did not know what was on the screen. Her mind was a million light years away from that programme. She was contemplating the future and it looked bleak.

She had to talk to someone about it all. But who? Her friend had not been interested. Her daughter was too young. Who could she turn to? But Sara already knew the answer: No-one. She had to deal with this herself. If she did not then no-one else would.

She went up to bed alone as usual that night. He would appear eventually. Too drunk to take off his clothes let alone give her the love and attention she so craved. Sara took out her lipstick and sat looking into the bedroom mirror for a few moments. She rocked back and forth gently yet tensely and shut her eyes and let her mind wander.

At first they were good thoughts. Louise playing in the garden, wide-eyed, face smiling. Other children looking happy and so contented. Then *HE* came on the scene. She could see his face angrily close up against her own. He was shouting abuse at her. Then he threw a punch.

She snapped out of her day dream and looked in the mirror once more. All she could see was a desperately unhappy face, lined with fear and misery. Sara twisted the bottom of the canister of lipstick so that the red tip slowly grew longer. She studied it for a second. Then she put it between her fingers like a pen and began to write on the mirror in front of their bed:

'Bastard Thornton. I hate you.'

*   *   *

Sara did not go to bed that night after all. It was still early. She was not going to give him the pleasure of knowing she would be waiting obediently in bed for his return. That had happened on too many occasions in the past.

This time she was going to surprise him. Sara tidied herself in front of that same mirror where she had just scrawled her desperate message of hate and walked out of the front door.

This time she was going to have a drink. She had been through enough. Why couldn't she enjoy herself for once. But Sara did not like being out for long. Within an hour she was back at the neatly kept house. He wasn't there. She felt so disappointed. She had hoped that perhaps he would get back and find her gone and start to think about the consequences of his actions.

But he had gone past the point of no return. He did not care. As she sat there downstairs in the tiny living room, she heard him scraping the front door lock with his key. She did not need to even see him to know he was drunk. Probably so inebriated he could not get that key in the lock at the first, second or even third attempt.

It must have taken ten goes before the key connected and the drunken mess stumbled through the doorway. He stood there for a moment and just stared at her. She wondered if perhaps he felt a twinge of guilt. Maybe even a little shame?

But Malcolm Thornton did not feel anything of the kind. His only thoughts were filled with hate. She seemed to be smirking at him. Making fun of him. Trying to make him feel guilty.

'What's your problem?'

He did not really care. He just did not like being

made to feel bad. But he would get his own back on her.

'Just come to bed Malcolm.'

Sara had given up on her husband. The message written on the mirror upstairs said it all. She wanted him to know how much hatred she felt towards him. He had made her life a misery. He had destroyed her future. What more could he do? Now he lay slumped on their sofa. A drunken hulk of a man once again incapacitated by the alcohol he craved for. Malcom Thornton wanted to escape. Soon he would escape for good.

'Well. I'm going to bed.'

Sara did not really know why she bothered saying the words. He was still collapsed on the sofa. He mumbled some obscenity at her but his lips could not keep pace with his brain. He was out of sync. When he spoke it was like an actor in one of those badly dubbed foreign films. His mind was filled with evil thoughts but he was having immense difficulties making his mouth work accordingly.

Then she heard the unmistakable words. The utterance that was totally unforgivable in her terms. The threat that shook her into action. So vicious that it convinced her utterly that he was no better than scum.

'Keep that daughter of yours out of my way or else she'll be dead meat.'

There was no mistaking his words. He had paused long and hard before saying it. No doubt he wanted to make sure he did not suffer his usual lip synch problems. He was determined to ensure that she heard it all.

'Keep that daughter of yours out of my way or else she'll be dead meat.'

Sara sat there in silence. She absorbed the words slowly. She could not comprehend it at first. What did her 10 year old daughter have to do with their problems? Why was he dragging her into this?

When it dawned on her, she was barely able to contain herself. She clenched both her hands into tight fists, struggling to stop her finger nails digging too deeply into the palms of her hands.

How dare he threaten my daughter. My only reason for living. My only happiness. My only joy.

Now she really understood him for the first time. Through all his dozens of drinking sessions and abuse he had never tried to involve Louise. Now he had crossed that final barrier. This was worse than all-out war. This was a warning about the safety of her only piece of true flesh and blood. He was putting her life at risk. He was daring to suggest that Louise could be in danger from him – the only other person living in that tiny house. Malcolm Thornton made it sound like he was pronouncing a death sentence on Louise. Actually, he was helping to guarantee his own.

'You fucking whore.'

Sara's drunken slob of a husband had just got a second wind. The tirade of insults that followed were far more audible than his earlier words. He had seen the look of shock and horror on her face after he made that threat to her daughter. Now he was going in for the kill with a flurry of blue obscenities that turned the atmosphere real.

Sara still sat there totally stunned by his bullying tactics. She wasn't really listening to the tirade of verbal abuse. Her mind was on one person – her darling little daughter who lay asleep just a few feet away. What if he meant it? What if he really did intend to do her harm? How could they live under the same roof with that threat hanging over? He was calling her little baby 'dead meat'. Sara was not going to risk it. She had to do something.

'Whore! Whore! Whore!'

Sara's silence seemed to inspire Malcolm Thornton to even nastier language. He was shouting at the top of his voice now. But the only words she heard were: 'Keep that daughter of yours out of my way or else she'll be dead meat.' This bastard was going to kill her daughter unless she did something. He was going to butcher her beautiful little girl. One day, when she was out he would creep up on Louise and murder her. But he would only be doing it to get at his wife. Louise would end up being the innocent victim of her mother's hatred for her husband.

Sara hated the feeling that she was responsible. It made her realise she had to act – fast!

She got up without saying a word and walked into the kitchen. The drunken lump was still continuing his stream of obscenities. He was oblivious to the fact she had left the room. He did not care. He just wanted to hurt her and Louise.

In the kitchen, she opened a drawer and found what she was looking for. It was one of their very best steak knives. Malcolm always wanted the best. Now he was going to get it. First she had to make sure it was going to do the job properly. Sara pulled out the knife sharpener and began, almost lovingly to scrape the knife over the rough edged metal. Each time, she would gently rub her thumb across the edge to see if it was definitely sharp enough. Finally, it was ready. In the lounge, Thornton was still shouting. But Sara had heard it all before. She was not going to hear it much longer.

She looked down at him one last time. She glanced at his bloated beer-filled stomach with disdain. He had dared to threaten the life of her daughter. Now he would pay the price.

But did she really want to kill him? Did she honestly want to take another person's life? Sara Thornton did not really know the answer to that herself. She stood with the specially sharpened knife waiting. Perhaps he would grab it off her? At least he would ward her off surely?

It was possible that for one strange moment she hoped he would stop her. After all, killing is not an easy task for anyone. It takes a lot of courage, fear and hatred.

She could not wait a moment longer. She plunged the knife into his soft protruding stomach and dug the six-inch blade in as far as it would go.

Suddenly a frenzy took over. She started to stab and stab and stab. Nothing could stop her now. The killing was done. Little Louise could live safely. He wouldn't get to her. He was not going to harm her.

'I've just killed my husband. I've stuck a six-inch carving knife in his belly.'

It was a matter-of-fact statement, with no emotion except, perhaps for a faint air of resignation.

Sara did not bother to wait until the emergency services arrived to make her confession. She told the operator after she had dialled 999. She had nothing to hide. She felt no shame. In fact she felt relief from the awful burden of living with a bullying brute who had plagued every working moment of her existence.

Still she felt as if she needed further re-assurance. She went to a cupboard and took out a camera. She wanted to record her husband's final dying moments. She wanted to have a record of the terror she had inflicted on him after years of being on the receiving end.

Sara looked at the bloody corpse of her 44 year old husband through the view-finder of the camera and pressed the shutter tight.

Click. She captured his dying moments.

Click. She watched as he bled to death.

Click. She saw him get exactly what he deserved.

The ambulancemen who showed up were astonished when they saw her taking the pictures. She couldn't give a damn. She just hoped that the judge would understand all the pain and suffering she had endured at her husband's hands.

In HM Prison Bullwood Hall more than two years later, Sara had discovered that there was no sympathy for a woman who kills her husband.

It was August 10, 1991, and 34 year old Sara was frail and weak from the hunger strike she vowed would continue until the Home Secretary promised to re-examine her case.

'I have no wish to die. I love life too much. But I cannot let this issue pass without making a stand. My life is all I have left to fight for.'

The judge at her trial at Birmingham Crown Court had not appreciated the pain and suffering she had endured. Sentencing her to life imprisonment, Mr Justice Igor Judge told Sara: 'You have been convicted of murder. The law permits only one sentence for murder, that you go to prison for life.'

In July 1991, her attempt to overturn the murder conviction in the Appeal Court had failed.

The hunger strike was Sara's last resort.

As her supporters waved placards and demanded a re-trial outside the prison, Sara doggedly refused to take any food for 20 days. She only decided to give up her fast when she was reunited with her daughter Louise who had moved to America to live with Sara's sister after her imprisonment.

'My daughter and I have a deep and unique relationship. If I die she won't have a mother.'

The Home Secretary has so far rejected all appeals for the case to be re-examined. Meanwhile, the campaign to free Sara goes on.

Wife killer Joe McGrail remains a free man.